Systematics and Morphology of the Antarctic Cranchiid Squid *Galiteuthis Glacialis* (Chun)

E. S. McSweeny

Paper 1 in

Biology of the Antarctic Seas VII
Antarctic Research Series Volume 27

David L. Pawson, Editor

American Geophysical Union

SYSTEMATICS AND MORPHOLOGY OF THE ANTARCTIC CRANCHIID SQUID *GALITEUTHIS GLACIALIS* (CHUN)

E. S. McSweeny

BIOLOGY OF THE ANTARCTIC SEAS VII
Antarctic Research Series Volume 27

Edited by David L. Pawson

Library of Congress Cataloging in Publication Data

McSweeny, E. S., 1934-
  Systematics and morphology of the Antarctic cranchiid squid Galiteuthis glacialis (Chun).

  (Biology of the Antarctic seas; 7, paper 1)
(Antarctic research series; v. 27)
  Cover title.
  Bibliography: p.
  1. Galiteuthis glacialis—Classification.
2. Galiteuthis glacialis—Anatomy. 3. Mollusks—
Classification. 4. Mollusks—Anatomy. 5. Mollusks
—Antarctic regions. I. Title. II. Series.
III. Series: American Geophysical Union. Antarctic
research series; v. 27.
QH95.58.B56 vol. 7, paper 1 [QL430.3.C72]
ISBN 0-87590-134-4 574.92′4s [594′.56] 77-29245

Published by the
AMERICAN GEOPHYSICAL UNION
with the aid of a grant from the
National Science Foundation
March 6, 1978

Printed by
THE WILLIAM BYRD PRESS, INC.
Richmond, Virginia

SYSTEMATICS AND MORPHOLOGY OF THE ANTARCTIC CRANCHIID SQUID *GALITEUTHIS GLACIALIS* (CHUN)

E. S. McSweeny[1]

Rosenstiel School of Marine and Atmospheric Science
University of Miami, Coral Gables, Florida 33124

Examination of material of *Crystalloteuthis glacialis* Chun, 1906, collected by the U.S.N.S. *Eltanin* in antarctic waters indicates that *Crystalloteuthis* Chun, based on this species, is a synonym of *Galiteuthis* Joubin, 1898. *Galiteuthis glacialis* is completely described and illustrated, and its morphological development from 4-mm to 495-mm mantle length is given. The taxonomic status of *Crystalloteuthis beringiana* Sasaki and *Galiteuthis aspera* Filippova is discussed.

INTRODUCTION

The oegopsid squid family Cranchiidae is a rather poorly known group, although it is well represented in terms of species. Studies of this group have been hindered by the gradual but extensive morphological transition which many species undergo prior to maturity and by the dearth of large or mature specimens in collections. The result has been confusion in the taxonomic literature, since many names are based on obviously juvenile specimens and nominal species often differ only in growth features. The advent of relatively large, high-speed midwater trawls has improved the situation somewhat by adding greatly to the material available. At the same time, many of the fragile cranchiids are damaged by these trawls, and thus their advantages are partially offset. In spite of this, significant and extensive collections are being made and should soon allow the family to be put in proper order.

Although numerous expeditions have worked in antarctic waters, knowledge of cranchiid squids from those regions is little more advanced than that from any other area. Prior to the 1960's the taxonomic literature for the region consisted almost in entirety of Chun's [1910] *Valdivia* monograph. In recent years, both Russian and U.S. vessels have worked these waters extensively, and very considerable additions have been made to the literature. Since 1962, when the National Science Foundation's research vessel U.S.N.S. *Eltanin* began to work the oceans that bound Antarctica, the cephalopods collected by this program have been gathered at the University of Miami's Rosenstiel School of Marine and Atmospheric Science. Work on this collection, under the direction of Gilbert L. Voss, has resulted in reevaluation of taxonomic characters and higher classifications [Roper and Young, 1967, 1968; Roper et al., 1969]. Continuing work has been on the reconciliation of collected material with published descriptions and on species distributions, with their determining factors [Roper, 1969].

This paper deals with the morphology and taxonomic considerations of the most abundant antarctic cranchiid squid, *Galiteuthis glacialis* (Chun). An analysis of the distribution of this species will follow in a later paper. It is hoped that the total work will aid in systematic studies of other antarctic cranchiids and in distributional studies of all antarctic pelagic cephalopods.

METHODS

Abbreviations of measurements of individual specimens and of indices are standard in cephalopod literature and are defined by Voss [1963] and Roper [1966]. Cranial width is defined as the maximum dorsal width of the cranial cartilage, where it flares over the eyes. The terminology of the mandibles is after Clarke [1962c] and Mangold and Fiorini [1966]. Because of the large number of specimens involved,

---

[1]Present address: Weyerhaeuser Co., Homestead, Florida 33030.

measurements of a selected series are given in condensed form in Table 3. The same series of measurements, presented as indices, is summarized in Table 4. Meristic characters are summarized in Table 5.

HISTORICAL REVIEW

The genus *Galiteuthis* was created by Joubin in 1898 to include a species represented by a moderately large (350-mm total length), relatively intact specimen. This specimen possessed the fused mantle connections of cranchiids, recognized at the time under the family name Cranchiaeformes, but also had hooks on the tentacular club, a character previously known only in the polyphyletic family Onychii. Joubin put heavy emphasis on this character and created a new family, the Cranchionychiae, to accept the genus, which he believed represented an intermediate form. It was soon recognized [Chun, 1906] that the fusion of the mantle with the head and funnel was of greater significance than the possession of hooks and that the genus belonged in the Cranchiidae. Several other species of *Galiteuthis* have since been added to the genus; these are open to question and have at one time or another been synonymized with Joubin's original species, *G. armata*.

In the second edition of his narrative account of the *Valdivia* expedition, Chun [1903, p. 232] briefly mentioned, among larger organisms taken by the vertical nets, stalk-eyed squids belonging to the family Cranchiidae. On the same page he figured such a squid, showing prominent tubercles at the dorsal fusion of the head and mantle. This figure is captioned, 'New genus of stalk-eyed squid of the family Cranchiidae' (translation). In 1906, Chun published a synopsis of the family Cranchiidae. In this paper he erected five new genera, all monotypic, which were characterized briefly in a key including all genera of the family. One of these new genera, *Crystalloteuthis*, was included in the division lacking cartilaginous ridges on the mantle and further separated into the group which lacks hooks on the tentacular club. The genus was characterized by the following features: spindle-shaped body; small, elongate fins; gladius extending posteriorly beyond the fins; oval eyes, borne on a short, thick stalk; tentacle without a keel; three fusion points of the mantle margin with cartilaginous tubercles; and pancreas extending to the caecum. The species on which the genus was based Chun named *glacialis*; its distribution was given as 'Antarctic.'

In 1910, Chun published a complete report on the cephalopods taken during the *Valdivia* expedition, and in this work, *Crystalloteuthis glacialis* was described and figured in considerable detail. In the synonymy, Chun referred to the figure in his 1903 work. The character which he noted primarily as separating the species from other cranchiids was the possession of complex cartilaginous tubercles at the fusion points of the mantle with the head. He felt that this feature indicated a connecting link between those cranchiids which possess tubercle-bearing cartilaginous strips and those which were of stalk-eyed form [Chun, 1910, p. 372]. Although his description of the single specimen does not add any new major characters to those listed in the previous publication, it is quite detailed and covers most features of the external and internal anatomy.

Hoyle [1910] included *Crystalloteuthis*, with the single species *glacialis*, in his list of generic names. Aside from affirming that the genus was monotypic, he made no comment.

Pfeffer's [1912] monograph included the species, although in what was apparently a slip of the pen, he applied the specific name *gracilis*. The name is spelled correctly in the synonymy. Pfeffer had no material of the species and relied entirely on Chun's description.

Abel [1916] discussed numerous aspects of living and fossil cephalopods. Although he included no systematic classification or discussion, he mentioned *Crystalloteuthis glacialis* several times in connection with the relation of morphological development to depth inhabited, swimming, feeding, etc.

Berry [1917], reporting on the Australasian Antarctic Expedition cephalopods, summarized the literature. He listed *Crystalloteuthis glacialis* among only 17 cephalopod (6 teuthoid) species known from south of 60°S. His material did not include the species, however.

Naef [1921a] included Chun's genus in his classification of dibranchiate cephalopods under the family Cranchiidae, but without discussion. During the same year the first volume of his cephalopod work in the series *Fauna and Flora of the Gulf of Naples* appeared. In this work he listed the genus incorrectly in the systematic synopsis as *Cristalloteuthis*. In 1922 his major work on fossil cephalopods was published. The genus *Crystalloteuthis*, correctly spelled this time, was again listed in the family Cranchiidae. In none of his publications did Naef mention the specific name, a reflection, presumably, of the monotypic status of the genus.

Grimpe also listed the generic name only, in both his sytematic review of European cephalopods [Grimpe, 1922] and his work on cephalopods of the North Sea [Grimpe, 1925].

Sasaki [1920] added another species to the genus *Crystalloteuthis* when he reported on the cephalopods collected in the North Pacific by the U.S. Fisheries steamer *Albatross*. This species, *C. beringiana*, was described only briefly, and the only characters given which readily distinguished it from *C. glacialis* were the absence of cartilaginous tubercles at the dorsal mantle fusion and the small number of tentacular stalk suckers. In his posthumously published monograph of Japanese dibranchiate cephalopods, Sasaki [1929] gave a diagnosis of the genus *Crystalloteuthis*. He listed the presence of tubercles at the mantle-funnel fusion as diagnostic and stated that the presence of dorsal tubercles was variable. He also stated that the tentacular armature was composed entirely of suckers, 'even at maturity,' and that fixing pads were not present on either the tentacular stalk or the carpal region. In this work the name of his species was spelled '*behringiana*' in the index as well as the text. There is no indication of a printer's or other error in the original publication, where the name appeared eight times, and no statement to that effect in the 1929 work. Therefore the original spelling must be retained, and the later usage, '*behringiana*,' considered an unjustified emendation (International Code of Zoological Nomenclature, article 33(a)). Sasaki's description in this work elaborated only slightly on his original treatment, although he illustrated the species in some detail.

The next appearance of the genus *Crystalloteuthis* in the literature was apparently Dell's [1959] report on the British and New Zealand Antarctic Research Expedition cephalopods, which included *C. glacialis*. Dell did not describe his material, but he listed five stations at which the species was taken. He made no mention of the northern extent of the species but gave the longitudinal distribution as 40°–143°E, at a depth of 750–1710 m.

Subsequently, Clarke [1966] published his 'Review of the Systematics and Ecology of Oceanic Squids.' His separation of the cranchiid subfamilies Cranchiinae and Taoniinae took into account only the presence or absence of cartilaginous tubercles at the funnel-mantle fusions and the number of ocular light organs and not the form of these characters. The first subfamily has cartilaginous tubercles located in strips on the mantle and small, discrete, round photophores, which are very different from the flattened organs of the Taoniinae, on the eyes. On this basis he incorrectly included *Crystalloteuthis* in the Cranchiinae. Clarke recognized that most of the characters in the descriptions of both species were juvenile but stated that both were 'distinguished from all other species by the possession of single cartilaginous tubercles at each of the funnel-mantle fusions.'

Roper [1969] briefly compared the distribution of *Crystalloteuthis glacialis* with that of *Bathyteuthis abyssicola*; he based this comparison on a preliminary survey of part of the material on which the present study is based.

Roper et al. [1969] mention the genus *Crystalloteuthis* only in correcting Clarke's [1966] subfamilial placement.

Nesis [1972, personal communication, 1972] suggested that *Crystalloteuthis* Chun, *Taonidium* Pfeffer, and *Zygocranchia* Hoyle were identical to *Galiteuthis* Joubin. He further stated that *Crystalloteuthis beringiana* Sasaki was a synonym of *Galiteuthis phyllura* Berry.

Filippova [1972] described a new species of *Galiteuthis*, *G. aspera*, from material trawled in the Scotia Sea.

SYSTEMATICS AND MORPHOLOGY

Galiteuthis Joubin, 1898

Galiteuthis Joubin, 1898, p. 279; Hoyle, 1904, p. 17; Chun, 1906, p. 86; 1910, p. 382; Hoyle, 1910, p. 409; Pfeffer, 1912, p. 731; Berry, 1912, p. 315; Naef, 1923, p. 398; Sasaki, 1929, p. 315; Akimushkin, 1963, p. 192; Clarke, 1966, p. 237; Nesis, 1972, p. 349; Young, 1972, p. 84.
Crystalloteuthis Chun, 1906, p. 85; 1910, p. 372; Hoyle, 1910, p. 408; Pfeffer, 1912, p. 726; Abel, 1916, pp. 36, 50; Sasaki, 1920, p. 202; Naef, 1921a, p. 536; 1922, p. 299; Grimpe, 1922, p. 51; 1925, p. 98; Sasaki, 1929, p. 323; Dell, 1959, p. 97; Akimushkin, 1963, p. 197; Clarke, 1966, p. 217; Roper et al., 1969, p. 13; Nesis, 1972, p. 349.
Cristalloteuthis Naef, 1921b, p. 49.

Type species. *Galiteuthis armata* Joubin, 1898; by monotypy.

Diagnosis. Cranchiid squids attaining moderately large size. Mantle fusiform, with greatest diameter in anterior third, tapering to a slender point posteriorly. Mantle wall very thin in juveniles, somewhat thicker and quite muscular in adults, the surface bearing sparsely scattered chromatophores and, in some, scattered cartilaginous tubercles. Fusion points of mantle with funnel and head may bear simple or complex cartilaginous tubercles. Fins separate, the combined shape lanceolate, minute in juvenile, with length approximately equal to width; becoming very elongate, to half or more of total mantle length, in adult. Head bearing large, globular eyes equipped with a broad semilunar photophore around the ventral circumference and a similar, smaller organ within the concavity of the larger. Cranial portion narrow, concave ventrally, flaring slightly over eyes dorsally. Eye capsule bears an 'olfactory organ' on the posteroventral surface, sessile in juveniles, slightly stalked in adults. Funnel short, broad at the base, tapering rapidly to a rather narrow tip, extended in juveniles, reflexed in adults. Dorsal member of funnel organ a rounded inverted V, with a conical papilla more or less developed at apex and the tip of each leg. Ventral members usually oval or slightly triangular. Arms short, thick, and muscular, with tips more or less attenuate, equipped with two rows of alternate suckers with inner rings toothed or smooth. Tentacles elongate, with clubs slightly expanded, armed with four rows of suckers, of which the proximal four to eight in the two center rows convert to hooks with growth. Club bordered dorsally and ventrally by low protective membranes, supported by weak trabeculae, which terminate proximal to carpal cluster. A minute dorsal keel is always present at the extreme tip of the club. Carpal cluster indistinguishable in juveniles, distinct but not bordered off in large individuals. Stalk bears a series of minute suckers arranged in staggered pairs, borne on elongate pedicels in juveniles, becoming recessed, but not sessile, with growth. Sucker pairs alternate with pairs of smooth pads. Gladius with extremely elongate, slender rachis and narrow vanes which arise laterally, turn under in posterior portion, and overlap but do not fuse. No conus present. Viscera greatly reduced. Liver elongate, spindle-shaped. Hepatopancreatic duct Y-shaped. Pancreas in two massive lobes at either side of dorsal end of liver, some species with diffuse follicles extending along hepatopancreatic duct to caecum. Caecum small, round. Stomach large, elongate, extending to posterior tip of mantle in larger specimens. Gonad single, median, lying on dorsal wall of stomach in posterior portion of mantle. Female reproductive apparatus paired, located immediately dorsal to branchial heart. Male reproductive apparatus single, located on anterior side of left branchial heart.

Discussion. The major character separating the genus *Crystalloteuthis* from *Galiteuthis* was the lack of tentacular hooks in the former. Chun recognized that juveniles of *Galiteuthis* possessed only suckers on the tentacular club and developed hooks at later stages [Chun, 1906, p. 86], but he believed, on the basis of his single small specimen, that *Crystalloteuthis* lacked hooks even as an adult. In addition, he placed great emphasis on the presence of complex cartilaginous tubercles at the fusion points of the mantle with the head and funnel.

Complex cartilaginous tubercles occur at the funnel-mantle fusion in several species of cranchiid squids, crossing well-established generic boundaries [Voss, 1967b; McSweeny, 1971]. During the course of this study they were observed in specimens of *Galiteuthis* from the North Atlantic, North Pacific, southeastern Pacific, and antarctic waters, as well as in the subject species *G. glacialis.* They may occur in all species of the genus. The form of the tubercles varies somewhat among species and may constitute a specific character. The complex tubercles found at the nuchal fusion in *G. glacialis* appear to be unique. A single, simple tubercle is present in *Mesonychoteuthis hamiltoni* [McSweeny, 1971], but other species appear to have the nuchal cartilage unarmed.

Examination of larger specimens of *G. glacialis* in the course of this study revealed that hooks are present in this species also. The hooks are indistinguishable from those figured by various authors for *Galiteuthis* but are of a different appearance from those found on the tentacles of *Mesonychoteuthis* or from the hooklike sucker dentition of *Taonius.*

The presence of pancreatic follicles along the hepatopancreatic duct is a character which should be surveyed throughout the Cranchiidae, as well as in a more extensive material of *Galiteuthis.* Of the comparative material examined, none showed this feature. In the literature it is reported only for *Desmoteuthis pellucida* Chun (1910), in addition to *G. glacialis.* The relative importance of this character cannot be fully evaluated on the basis of the material seen, but in the absence of supporting characters it cannot be considered of generic value.

A careful examination was made of the material included in this study to determine whether any characters were present which warranted the retention of a separate genus. Comparison was made with published accounts of other authors and with specimens of *Galiteuthis* available in the collections of the Rosenstiel School of Marine and Atmospheric Science. No such characters were found, and the only possible conclusion is that *Crystalloteuthis* Chun, 1906, is a junior synonym of *Galiteuthis* Joubin, 1898, as was proposed by Nesis [1972].

Galiteuthis glacialis (Chun, 1906)
Figs. 1–8

New genus of family Cranchiidae, Chun, 1903, p. 232 (figure).

Crystalloteuthis glacialis Chun, 1906, p. 85; 1910, p. 372, pl. 53, figs. 2–9, pl. 54, fig. 18; Hoyle, 1910, p. 408; Abel, 1916, pp. 34, 63, 91; Berry, 1917, p. 6; Sasaki, 1929, p. 324; Dell, 1959, p. 97; Akimushkin, 1963, p. 197; Clarke, 1966, p. 217; Roper, 1969, p. 188.

Crystalloteuthis gracilis Pfeffer, 1912, p. 726; Sasaki, 1929, p. 325.

Galiteuthis aspera Filippova, 1972, p. 400.

Location of type specimen. Unknown.

Diagnosis. Mantle smooth in juveniles, bearing numerous rounded cartilaginous tubercles scattered randomly over surface in adults. Fins broadly lanceolate, extending to tip of gladius. Funnel-mantle fusion with five- to seven-pointed cartilaginous tubercles, with points arranged in two longitudinal series. Nuchal fusion with pair of two- to three-pointed tubercles, with points in a single longitudinal row. Larger ocular photophore extending around half or more of ventral circumference of eye, small photophore only slightly curved, becoming bar-shaped in adult. Dorsal member of funnel organ with well-developed conical, apical papilla. Papillae at tip of posterior legs becoming larger, slightly flattened laterally, with growth. Arm suckers dentate, the teeth becoming sharper, fewer in number toward tip. Tentacular stalk suckers number 50–60 at all mantle lengths, club hooks number 10–12 in mature animal. Hook insertion plates two- to four-digitate. Dactylus suckers armed with two to four blunt teeth.

Material Examined

The material of *G. glacialis* examined in the course of this study consisted of 824 specimens from 244 stations, as listed in Tables 1 and 2. This material all originated from *Eltanin* collections, mostly those made by the University of Southern California (USC) biological sampling program. Specimens taken by the 3-m Isaacs-Kidd Midwater Trawl are shown in Table 1 in numerical order for the USC stations, followed by those from other programs. Collections made with other gear are shown in Table 2. Other programs which captured material are identified in this paper as SC (Smithsonian Oceanographic Sorting Center), LGO (Lamont-Doherty Geological Observatory), or TAM (Texas A&M University) or are self-defined. Station information can be obtained from Savage and Caldwell [1965, 1966] and the University of Southern California [1967] reports or from the Supervisor for Records, Smithsonian Oceanographic Sorting Center, Washington, D. C.

Description

Gross morphology. The mantle is elongate and slender (mantle width index (MWI) = 14.0–18.0) and is widest in the anterior third, gradually tapering posteriorly to a slender point (Figure 1). The muscular portion is reduced in the anterior quarter of the fins until it is only a thin sheath around the gladius.

The mantle wall is very thin and consists of four layers, with a complex structure (Figure 2). The innermost layer is very thin and loosely attached, peeling off easily in preserved material. The major portion of the mantle is a muscular layer composed of transverse sheets of loose muscle fibers contained between thin, transverse muscular septa. The figures by Chun [1910, Plate LIV, Figures 9 and 10] of the mantle of *Desmoteuthis pellucida* illustrate the structure of the muscular layer very well. This muscular portion is actually two layers, since the septa extend only slightly past the center of the layer, interconnecting with septa proceeding from the opposite surface [Chun, 1910, Figure 10]. The muscular portion is not continuous over the gladius in the dorsal midline. External to the muscular portion is a moderately thick, spongy layer which is tightly anchored to the outer portion of the muscular layer

TABLE 1.   Material of *Galiteuthis glacialis* Examined in This Study Which Was Collected With the 3-m Isaacs-Kidd Midwater Trawl

TABLE 1.   (continued)

Station	Number of Specimens	Size Range, mm
University of Southern California		
131	9	16 31
132	1	72
133	8	15–27
137	6	24–39, 82
141	22	22–38
142	3	24, 38, 112
143	7	18–29
248	1	56
259	1	43
262	1	44
274	1	55
279	1	35
280	1	44
282	1	237
285	1	37
292	1	34
302	4	5.5–43
318	1	11
319	1	12
348	1	38
364	13	37–64
368	9	7–60
379	1	20
396	4	4–7
397	2	9, 9
414	2	18, 59
422	2	17, 58
449	1	10
563	1	36
567	2	13, 120
575	2	9, 12
580	1	20
581	2	46, 74
593	6	14–21
597	1	80
601	11	12–48
611	1	42
627	1	28
640	1	14
642	1	13
643	3	8, 8, 56
653	2	27, 51
683	2	26, 28
687	1	95
696	1	25
697	1	29
701	1	38
702	2	35, 43
703	1	80
714	1	34
730	3	21–34
737	1	43
738	1	35
792	3	34–53
793	2	29, 36
796	1	52
802	7	28–41
811	12	29–56, 138
812	5	30–47
831	5	4–29
847	1	133

Station	Number of Specimens	Size Range, mm
University of Southern California (continued)		
854	1	48
855	3	46–50
865	2	9, 48
888	1	63
890	2	33, 53
891	1	6
892	1	48
895	1	49
898	1	58
903	1	7
904	1	56
911	2	10, 182
912	2	7, 66
914	3	9, 10, 89
917	6	9–15
918	2	7.5, 9.5
919	1	12
920	1	8
922	2	12, 12
929	2	11, 13
932	4	14–15, 75
933	4	12–58, 496
935	9	13–69
936	4	12–65
940	5	13–68
941	1	?
943	23	10–87
944	3	11–54
946	6	10–17
947	6	11–70
949	11	13–88
950	8	12–93
953	1	63
998	1	53
1006	2	11, 44
1014	4	11–14
1019	3	10, 33, 107
1022	1	13
1023	4	16–52, 107
1026	5	13–35
1027	4	8–50
1029	12	7–15
1030	1	37
1036	8	9–58, 178
1038	4	10–37
1050	21	10–49
1051	1	36
1057	5	8–47
1064	4	10–44, 105
1065	8	15–51
1071	1	115
1072	1	24
1076	3	13–93
1077	4	14–96
1112	1	395
1114	2	34, 45
1121	3	14–27
1129	3	17–26
1133	3	22–72
1137	2	18, 29
1142	1	32
1162	5	21–27
1163	3	23–35

TABLE 1.   (continued)

Station	Number of Specimens	Size Range, mm
University of Southern California (continued)		
1170	1	51
1213	2	23, 207
1238	1	22
1241	1	24
1242	1	27
1244	34	20–39
1247	1	28
1269	2	46, 64
1290	3	35–67
1299	1	38
1303	3	52–70
1306	1	25
1323	1	333
1324	1	62
1348	1	29
1359	1	237
1376	3	54–57
1388	1	169
1392	1	163
1393	1	127
1483	1	37
1485	3	14–34
1486	19	13–35
1488	33	13–41
1507	1	63
1510	4	57–63
1512	3	39–69
1518	1	17
1522	1	13
1528	1	130
1546	2	35, 40
1550	1	38
1559	4	7–35
1586	1	78
1615	1	32
1633	1	39
1634	2	35, 130
1637	1	50
1641	1	84
1648	1	32
1649	1	52
1665	1	65
1676	3	14–24
1678	3	49, 56, 174
1679	1	41
1683	1	23
1684	2	26, 30
1689	4	25–43, 228
1936	2	27, 37
1970	2	14, 18
1971	1	16
1976	1	18
2077	1	35
2111	2	51, 119
2122	2	39, 42
2131	1	13
2133	2	42, 52
2140	3	13–21
2168	1	87
2174	3	18–125
2177	1	158
2260	5	13–43
2262	13	30–45

TABLE 1.   (continued)

Station	Number of Specimens	Size Range, mm
University of Southern California (continued)		
2263	1	41
2264	2	49, 87
2266	1	65
2294	6	38–56
2297	3	26–33
DePaul University		
19-23	1	11
19-29	2	17, 22
Smithsonian Sorting Center		
SC 3-14	1	17
SC 6-18	7	18–64
SC 7-20	20	17–23
SC 9-26	2	16, 25
SC 10-29	2	20, 22
SC 11-32	31	15–26
SC 12-34	9	19–24
SC 14-41	3	17–60
SC 17-47	9	13–22
SC 17-49	6	15–55
SC 19-52	7	17–26
SC 20-54	6	13–78
SC 21-56	1	18
SC 22-59	5	14–82
SC 23-61	5	13–25
SC 24-62	4	19–38
SC 25-63	1	19
SC 27-66	1	23
SC 34-86	1	42
SC 115	1	27
SC 118	4	20–33
SC 129	4	20–33
SC 133	1	30
SC 139	12	23–55
SC 140	5	30–48
SC 145	4	22–28
SC 151	3	29–45
SC 154	1	21

Size range is based on mantle length. Mantle lengths of larger specimens are listed individually.

by rootlike projections of connective tissue, which penetrate deeply between the septa and branch widely. The outermost layer of the mantle is a thin, dense tissue which appears to be composed of a few muscular elements covered by a thin epithelium. This layer is widely separated from the spongy layer. In larger specimens the mantle bears numerous cartilaginous tubercles scattered over the surface. These are more numerous anteriorly and dorsally, but in large animals they extend beyond the leading edge of the fins. The tubercles originate as thickenings in the external mantle layer, later becoming attached to the spongy layer. They are gradually replaced by cartilage, eventually becoming thick, pillarlike tuber-

TABLE 2. Material of *Galiteuthis glacialis* Examined in This Study Which Was Collected With Gear Other Than the 3-m Isaacs-Kidd Midwater Trawl

Station	Number of Specimens	Size Range, mm	Gear
298	1	27	Menzies trawl
462	1	9	Menzies trawl
523	1	83	Menzies trawl
564	1	25	Menzies trawl
828	1	43	5-foot Blake trawl
869	1	216	Rock dredge
951	1	231	5-foot Blake trawl
992	1	235	5-foot Blake trawl
1363	1	38	Rock dredge
1490	1	12	1-m Isaacs-Kidd midwater trawl
1638b	1	71	1/2-m plankton net
1941	2	23, 25	5-foot Blake trawl
LGO 371	1	297	Hydro wire
LGO 394	1	240	Hydro wire
SC 4-16	1	20	1-m Isaacs-Kidd midwater trawl
SC 8-24	1	49	5-foot Blake trawl
SC 8-25	2	15, 19	1-m Isaacs-Kidd midwater trawl
SC 21-58	1	15	1-m Isaacs-Kidd midwater trawl
SC 286	1	13	Plankton net
LGO 489	1	20	Bé net
LGO 504	1	25	Bé net
TAM 1768	1	26	Bé net

Stations are University of Southern California unless otherwise identified. LGO denotes Lamont-Doherty Geological Observatory; SC, the Smithsonian Oceanographic Sorting Center; and TAM, Texas A&M University.

cles, rounded distally, which may measure as much as 0.4 mm in diameter and 0.6 mm high. The prominence of the papillae increases with growth, giving the mantle a 'shaggy' appearance in larger specimens. The outer mantle layer is supported by these tubercles, fusing to them at the rounded shoulders, and they become deeply embedded in the spongy layer. There appears to be only an empty space between the spongy layer and the outer layer, which presumably is filled with liquid or a jellylike matrix. The outer layer becomes very transparent in large animals and rubs off easily; on most specimens it is lost in capture. The function of the tubercles or the space around them is unknown.

The anterior margin of the mantle is even around its circumference and fused dorsally to the head in the nuchal region and ventrolaterally to each side of the funnel. The nuchal fusion is marked by a rather broad, triangular cartilaginous plate, with the apex directed posteriorly along the center line (Figure 3d). The two lateral angles of this plate, along the anterior margin, each bear a small two- or three-pointed tubercle, with the largest point posterior. The two ventral points of fusion with the funnel are marked by narrow cartilaginous plates which taper posteriorly (Figure 3c). At the anterior margin of the mantle these plates bear a complex four- to six-pointed tubercle.

The fins are short and rounded in smaller specimens (fin length index (FLI) = 5.0–11.0 at 10- to 20-mm mantle length (ML)), becoming long and lanceolate in large ones (FLI = 40.0–45.0 at 300- to 400-mm ML). They lack free anterior lobes and taper to a slender point posteriorly. The width is less than half the length (fin width index (FWI) = 15.0–20.0). The fins are separate, and the muscular portion attaches at the dorsolateral margins of the shell sac, while the spongy layer and epithelium continue across the dorsal surface. The two muscle layers are composed of freely anastomosing transverse bundles, separated by sheets of radial fibers. Both portions are thicker, containing many more fibers than are in the same layers of the mantle. In addition, the two layers are separated horizontally by a thin sheet of longitudinal fibers.

The head is short, and the width consists mostly of the large, globular eyes (head width index (HWI) = 15.0). The central cranial portion is small and compressed, serving chiefly as a base for the eyes. The cranial portion comprises about one third of the total head width, at a point where it flares dorsally over the eyes, and is considerably narrower anteriorly. Ventrally, this portion is deeply concave, forming a groove in which the free portion of the funnel lies. The eyes are extremely large (eye diameter index (EDI) = 7.0–10.0) and extend well below the cranial portion of the head. They are directed laterally at an angle of approximately 60° with the longitudinal axis, so that the head is much wider in the posterior portion. The eye opening is greatly contracted in most specimens but is relatively small, appearing to be less than one quarter of the diameter. Although usually obscured owing to contraction, the pupil has a small anterior notch, or sinus. The center of the posterior surface of the eye bears a small cup-shaped olfactory organ, slightly stalked in larger specimens.

The eye bears two photophores on the ventral and lateral surfaces (Figure 1c). The larger of these extends around the ventral periphery of the eyeball, from the base of arms III on the anterior side to the midpoint of the posterior margin. It is crescent-shaped, covering most of the ventral surface of the

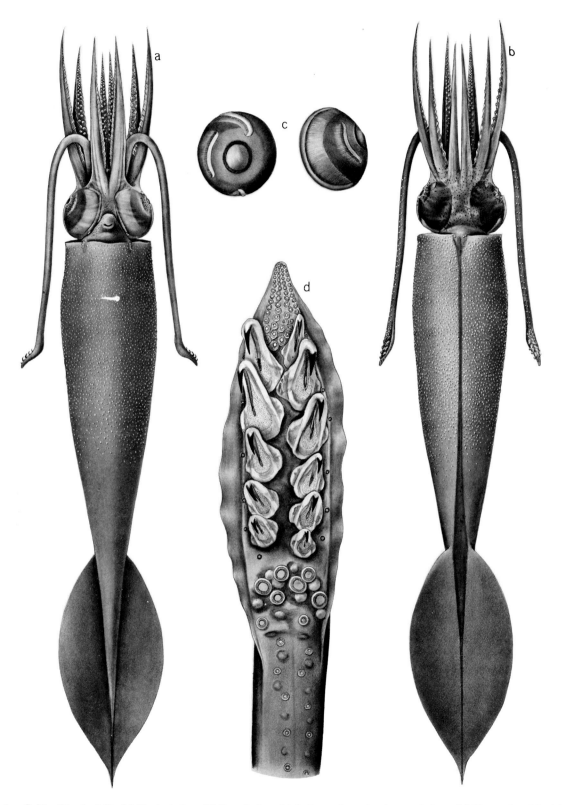

Fig. 1.   *Galiteuthis glacialis.* (*a*) Ventral view. (*b*) Dorsal view. (*c*) Left eye, lateral and ventral views. (*d*) Tentacular club. (*a*)–(*c*) ELT 1323, female, 333-mm ML. (*d*) ELT H-371, male, 297-mm ML.

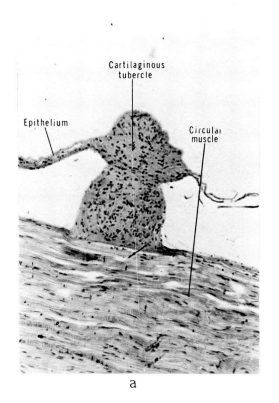

a

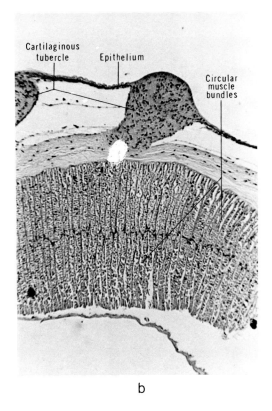

b

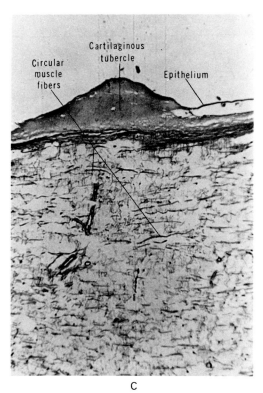

c

Fig. 2. *Galiteuthis glacialis*, histological sections. (*a*) Transverse section through mantle, ELT 1112, 395-mm ML. (*b*) Longitudinal section through mantle, ELT H-371, 297-mm ML. (*c*) Transverse section through mantle of gravid female, ELT 933, 496-mm ML.

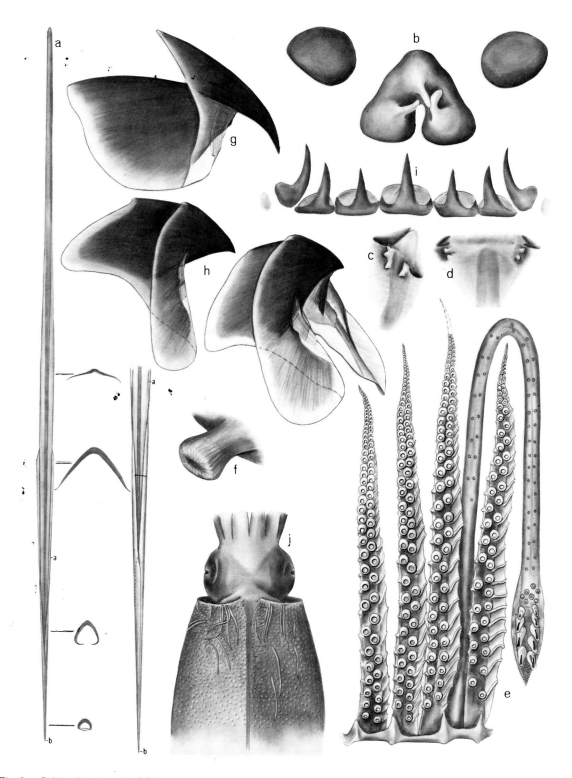

Fig. 3. *Galiteuthis glacialis.* (*a*) Gladius (ventral view). (*b*) Funnel organ. (*c*) Funnel-mantle fusion tubercles. (*d*) Nuchal fusion tubercles. (*e*) Brachial circlet (left side), oral view. (*f*) Olfactory tubercle. (*g*) Upper mandible. (*h*) Lower mandible. (*i*) Radula. (*j*) Dorsal view of gravid female showing attached sperm reservoirs. (*a*) ELT 943, female, 286-mm ML. (*b*)–(*f*) ELT 1323, female, 333-mm ML. (*g*)–(*i*) ELT H-371, male, 297-mm ML. (*j*) ELT 933, female, 496-mm ML.

eye, the ends turning slightly inward toward the pupil. The smaller photophore lies in the concavity of the crescent of the large organ, on the lateral surface of the eye. It is crescent or bar-shaped and shows the same structure as the large organ. In large specimens, only the thickened medial margin and a narrow band of lateral tissue are readily visible in either organ. These may change in various states of preservation but usually have a metallic sheen.

The funnel is short and tapers rapidly from a wide base. Only the distal quarter is free, and it lies in the groove on the ventral surface of the head, between the eyes. The distal portion of the dorsal wall turns ventrally to form a cuplike hood, while the ventral wall invariably has a deep, transverse fold, so the rather narrow tip is reflexed and pointing posteriorly. Its anterior extent decreases with growth, and in large specimens it reaches only to the midpoint of the eyes.

The funnel organ is variable, depending partly on the state of preservation. The dorsal member is in the form of an inverted U, broad and somewhat angular at the closed end (Figure 3b). The posterior arms of the U are angled slightly outward. An elongate, conical papilla is present in the center of the anterior portion, and a slightly shorter and thicker papilla is located on the distal portion of each arm. The two ventral pads are small and broad, rounded on the lateral margins and slightly angled on the inner margin. There is no trace of a funnel valve, although the flexion of the ventral wall could serve that function.

A narrow canal opens laterally on either side between the lower surface of the head and the dorsal funnel wall. It leads into a paired series of glandlike cavities directly dorsal to the lateral lobes of the dorsal funnel organ member. The nature and function of these organs and their canals are unknown. The openings may be homologous to the median orifice in the posterior funnel groove described by Roper [1968, 1969] in *Bathyteuthis*.

The arms are short, slender, and muscular, with the formula 4 = 3 > 2 > 1. There are weak aboral keels present on all arms, and a weak lateral keel on arms IV. Trabeculate protective membranes are present on all arms and are prominent on the ventral side. The arms bear biserial, stalked, globular suckers with large apertures that have the chitinous ring armed with a few teeth in the distal quarter (Figure 4). The dentition is barely apparent on the basal suckers, consisting of small but regular incisions in the distal portion of the inner ring, forming 5-10 square or slightly rounded teeth. The suckers increase in size toward the midportion of the arms, and the teeth become more numerous until they number 10-12. At the twenty-eighth to thirtieth sucker from the base of the arm the teeth abruptly decrease in number to 6-8, becoming long, curved, and sharp. Distally, the suckers decrease in size, and the teeth decrease in number and become blunter. The distal suckers bear 4-5 blunt, rounded teeth.

The tentacles are long and slender, with short, slightly expanded clubs (Figure 3e). The stalk is rounded aborally, with the oral surface flattened. The distal three quarters of the oral surface bears a series of 48-60 minute suckers, arranged in staggered pairs which are widely separated proximally but close together distally and alternating with pairs of smooth pads. The chitinous rings of these suckers are unarmed. The frequency with which given numbers of sucker pairs were observed is shown in Table 5.

The eight to ten suckers of the carpal fixing apparatus are abruptly larger, with deeply cupped, papillated outer rings and smooth chitinous rings, and are accompanied laterally by well-defined, rounded pads (Figure 1). The carpal apparatus of small specimens is indistinguishable from the tentacular series (see discussion of development). The lateral position of the pads alternates with the suckers, being dorsal in one pair and ventral in the next. The carpal apparatus of one tentacle is a mirror image of the other, with rare exceptions. The club is slightly expanded in the carpal region and widest in the middle of the manus, while the dactylus tapers rather abruptly to a point. Armament consists of four longitudinal rows of suckers, with the first five or six suckers in each of the two central rows transformed into prominent, sharp hooks (Figure 4h). The hooks are partially covered by thin, fleshy hoods. This modification first appears at about 60-mm ML. The suckers of the two outer rows of the manus are very small and are armed with three to five blunt, prominent teeth. They have broad, papillated outer rings.

The dactylus comprises one third of the club length, with the proximal suckers slightly smaller than the largest carpal suckers. The stalked suckers have hemispherical chitinous rings, very deep in the distal half and armed around the circumference with four to eight blunt teeth which are more prominent in the distal half. The papillated outer ring is very broad, with the distal half elongate, concave and

Fig. 4.　*Galiteuthis glacialis.* (*a*) Sucker rings from (left to right) fourth, twentieth, thirty-sixth, and seventieth suckers from base of arm II and (*b*) same series from arm IV. ELT 933, female, 496 mm. (*c*)–(*g*) Developmental series from tentacular club. Rings from largest manus sucker and associated marginal sucker. (*c*) 29-mm ML (ELT 697). (*d*) 38-mm ML (SC 24-62). (*e*) 55-mm ML (ELT 935). (*f*) 58-mm ML (ELT 949). (*g*) 73-mm ML (ELT 943). (*h*) Largest tentacular hook, ELT H-371, male, 297-mm ML.

turned downward over the chitinous ring. The club is bordered both dorsally and ventrally by wide protective membranes supported by broad, indistinct trabeculae. These membranes commence at the level of the most distal stalk sucker, are broadest in the manus region and narrower distally, and continue to the tip of the dactylus. The dactylus bears a minute dorsal keel at the tip.

The buccal mass is surrounded by concentric 'lips.' The inner is thick, and its distal surface is heavily papillated. The outer lip is smooth, and thick at the base, but much thinner distally where it closely sheathes the margin of the papillated inner lip. The buccal membrane has seven lappets, the connectives of which attach dorsally to arms I and II and ventrally to arms III and IV (Figure 3e).

The upper mandible (Figure 3g) has a slender, curved rostrum, smoothly rounded dorsally and comprising one third of the hood length. The internal surface of the rostrum is concave and smooth. The lateral margins of the inner surface continue across the wings in a very weak ridge. The wings extend downward to the ventral margin of the lateral wall, the posterior margins forming an even concave curve. The fusion between the lateral wall and the wing is narrow and does not extend to the ventral margin, leaving a small portion of the wing free. The shoulder is straight along the anterolateral margin but is armed with an obtuse projection of the lateral wall on the anterior surface, slightly to the inside. The jaw angle is a little less than 90°, while the angle between the hood and the crest (measured between lines connecting the tip of the rostrum with the posterior dorsal extremities of the hood and the crest) is about 30°. The hood length is approximately 75% of the crest length.

The hood of the lower mandible (Figure 3h) is short, the rostrum comprising about 75%. The posterior margin of the hood continues downward laterally in a convex curve to form the posterior margin of the wings. The wings are broad and rounded ventrally, and they project below the lateral wall by a distance equal to one fifth of the depth of the entire mandible. The shoulders are smooth and bulge anteriorly, forming a straight margin which obscures the jaw angle. The jaw angle is obtuse and rather sharp and is formed by an anterior projection of the lateral wall. This projection is more darkly colored than the surrounding chitin and terminates abruptly at the midpoint of the shoulder. The hood is one half to two thirds of the length of the crest, and the angle between the two is about 20°.

The radula (Figure 3i) has a broad, tricuspid rachidian tooth, with a long median and very small outer cusps. The first lateral has a broad base, with a long inner cusp centrally situated and a small outer cusp at the lateral margin. The second lateral is narrower, and its single long cusp is approximately equal in size to that of the first lateral. The third lateral bears a single long, slender cusp, equal in length to the median rachidian cusp. All of the long cusps are strongly curved forward on the ribbon. The marginals are barely visible as oval, unarmed disks.

The gladius (Figure 3a) is extremely slender, with a long, narrow rachis and narrow vanes. The rachis is rounded and thinner anteriorly and inserts into a cavity in the nuchal cartilage which extends to the anterior margin of the mantle. It is weakly convex dorsally and slightly thicker in the center than at the margins. It widens gradually posteriorly, becoming at the same time thicker and more strongly arched. The curved cross section gradually gives way to an inverted V shape. The widest point of the rachis is at the anterior margin of the fins, where it is very thick and steeply ridged. The vanes commence just behind the anterior fin margin. They widen gradually in the first third of the fins and then turn abruptly under, forming a flat lip which becomes proportionally wider as the rachis narrows to the posterior tip. In the posterior third of the fins the lateral margins of the rachis come very close together as the gladius becomes somewhat compressed laterally. The vanes overlap ventrally but appear never to fuse across the ventral surface to form a true conus, and this portion is here termed a 'pseudoconus.' The ventral concavity of the rachis can be distinguished almost to the posterior tip.

The gills are very small in relation to the size of the animal (gill length index (GLI) = 4.0–9.0) and are quite broad, with the width nearly half the length. They consist of about 23 or 24 pairs of filaments in specimens over 125-mm ML and somewhat fewer in smaller specimens (Table 5 and Figure 13). The inner demibranch is only about one half of the length of the outer but is well developed. It is supported by a cartilaginous stylet to which a branch of the afferent blood vessel is attached. The outer demibranch is fused distally to the base of the gill. The branchial gland is quite well developed. The branchial canal is almost completely occluded by the close-packed filaments of both demibranchs. The efferent branchial vessel receives the vessels from the filaments at right angles, in contrast to most other species examined, in which the vessels from individual filaments joined the main vessel at an acute angle.

Chromatophores were not visible in most of the preserved material, but observations on some fresh specimens plus several preserved animals in which chromatophores were still visible make it possible to give a partial description of the color pattern.

The chromatophores appear to be predominantly of two colors, a reddish brown and a very dark brown, which lie in different layers. The darker ones tend to be smaller, and several are very constant in position. The dorsal surface of the head bears two dark chromatophores on the midline, with several smaller ones scattered over the rest of the surface. The head bears two more dark chromatophores on the ventral midline and one at the base of each tentacle. Each eye bears an extremely large, reddish brown chromatophore on the dorsal surface, another on the ventral surface, and several smaller ones scattered on the anterior surface. There are numerous other reddish brown chromatophores on the dorsal surface of the head, on the dorsal surface of the funnel, on the base of the arms and their aboral surface, and around the outer surface of the buccal lobes. The tentacles bear a few large transverse, reddish brown chromatophores on the aboral surface, giving a striking banded appearance. Smaller, more numerous ones appear on the aboral surface of the club. Chun's figure [Chun, 1910, Plate LIII, Figure 5] is quite representative of the general appearance.

The few mantle chromatophores are mostly of the large reddish brown type and appear to be arranged in transverse rows of 10–12 around the anterior half. They are slightly smaller and closer together on the ventral surface. Posteriorly, the rows break down, and the arrangement seems to be random.

There are undoubtedly more chromatophores present in life than are described here, but the total number is small, and the overall impression of the live animals is one of extreme transparency.

Membranes and mantle chambers. The mantle is divided into several chambers by a series of thin, transparent membranes. The arrangement of these membranes is exceedingly difficult to make out in dissections because of their extreme transparency and fragility. Serial sections plus careful dissections were used to determine their lines of attachment and relative position. These are shown diagrammatically in Figure 5.

Essentially, the mantle can be considered a cone which sometimes is more or less inflated in the mid-portion. The anterior half of the cone is divided horizontally by a relatively thick membrane. Near the midpoint the membrane curves upward, joining with the upper portion of the mantle wall to close off the anterior upper half of the mantle. All the space below and posterior to this membrane, which communicates with the exterior, forms the exhalant chamber. Above this membrane the upper chamber is divided in the sagittal plane by a pair of thin membranes which attach dorsally along the margins of the shell sac and ventrally along the midline of the horizontal membrane. The spaces lateral to this pair of membranes form the two inhalant chambers. The anterior openings of the inhalant chambers are covered by a membranous valve which prevents the expulsion of water. The inhalant chambers connect with the exhalant chambers by semicircular openings covered by valvelike flaps of tissue to which the gills are attached. These flaps allow water to pass only in a posterior direction, into the exhalant chamber. The chamber formed between the sagittal membranes is the visceropericardial coelom. It is divided near the midportion of the mantle by the liver, which projects ventrally through the horizontal membrane in this region. The visceropericardial coelom penetrates the horizontal membrane where the latter curves dorsally. Behind this membrane there is no ventral support for the coelom, which is still attached dorsally along the margins of the shell sac and hangs free in the exhalant chamber. It continues into the distal tip of the mantle. Anteriorly, the exhalant chamber opens through the funnel between the funnel-mantle fusion points. The dorsal funnel wall is continuous with the dorsal wall of the exhalant chamber. The ventral wall projects into the exhalant chamber for a short distance, with the lateral margins fused to the ventral mantle wall. During expulsion of water from the exhalant chamber the ventral funnel wall is pressed against the mantle, forcing all water to exit through the funnel.

The nephridial sac is a single chamber on the posterior side of the liver, ventral to the visceropericardial coelom where the latter rejoins after passing around the liver. It extends ventrally to the distal third of the liver and is drawn out in two tubular lateral extensions to enclose the branchial hearts at the base of the gills. The kidney and vena cavae lie within this chamber on the posterior surface of the liver. The nephridial sac connects with the visceropericardial coelom by a pair of lateral canals which commence on either side of the superior lobe of

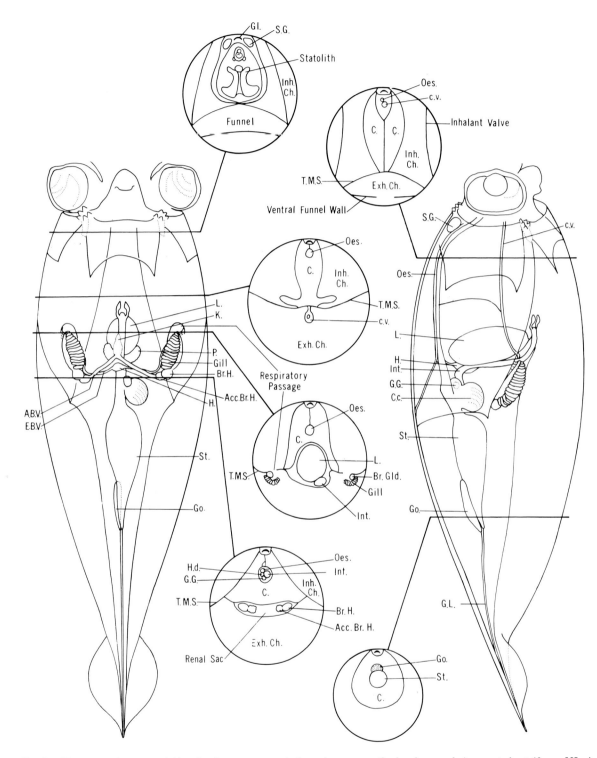

Fig. 5. Diagrammatic representation showing arrangement of membranes, mantle chambers, and viscera at about 40-mm ML. A. B. V. is the afferent branchial vessel; Acc. Br. H., accessory branchial heart; Br. Gld., branchial gland; Br. H., branchial heart; C., coelom; Cc., caecum; C. V., cephalic vein; E. B. V., efferent branchial vessel; Exh. Ch., exhalant chamber; G. G., gastric ganglion; Gl., gladius; G. L., gastrogenital ligament; Go., gonad; H., systemic heart; H. d., hepatopancreatic duct; Inh. Ch., inhalant chamber; Int., intestine; K., kidney; L., liver; Oes., esophagus; P., pancreas; S. G., stellate ganglion; St., stomach; T. M. S., transverse mantle septum.

the kidney and run dorsally and slightly anteriorly. It communicates with the exhalant chamber through a pair of nephridial pores, which are minute openings with slightly thickened rims, located directly ventral to the posteroventral end of the canals.

Digestive tract. The pharyngeal cavity is almost completely occupied by the odontophore and the palantine lobes. The odontophore bears the radular sac in its median dorsal surface. Below the radular sac it projects anteriorly in a salivary papilla, or 'tongue.' The palatine lobes enfold the odontophore on either side, forming a deep groove. They are covered with a thin chitinous layer which bears small teeth that are directed posteriorly on the inner surface at the tips. The esophagus originates as a continuation of the groove formed by the palatine lobes at the posterior termination of the pharynx.

Bidder [1966] listed five glands opening into the buccal cavity: the single median submandibular, or sublingual, gland; the paired anterior salivary glands; and the paired posterior salivary glands. The submandibular gland in this species is a small, compact gland occupying the anterior ventral portion of the odontophore below the salivary papilla. Its function is unknown [Bidder, 1966]; however, it is remarkably similar in structure to the salivary glands. The anterior salivary glands are wholly embedded in the posterior ventral portion of the buccal mass just behind the termination of the radular sac and anterior to the commencement of the esophagus. Their ducts run forward through the palatine lobes to open on the inner surface near the anterior end. The posterior salivary glands lie at the level of the stellate ganglia in the most anterior portion of the mantle, in the midline just below the esophagus. The glands are closely appressed, with the appearance of a single organ, and are separated only at the posterior end. A relatively large lumen runs the length of each gland, although it loses its identity in the posterior portion. These join in the anterior portion, emerging as a single duct. The duct runs anteriorly, just to the left of the esophagus, as far as the buccal mass, in which it becomes embedded in the ventral midline. It continues anteriorly, ventral to the radular sac, to open at the tip of the salivary papilla.

The esophagus proceeds posteriorly from the buccal mass, passing through the cephalic cartilage, and then runs upward slightly to a position close below the gladius at the anterior mantle margin. From this point it proceeds in a straight line to the dorsal tip of the liver, passing above the latter in the midline.

Just behind the liver the esophagus joins the intestine in a slightly enlarged chamber which Chun [1910] termed 'magensinus' and Bidder [1966] termed 'vestibule.' Slightly behind the junction of esophagus and intestine the vestibule connects with the caecum through an opening in the ventral wall, and posteriorly, it expands into the stomach (Figures 6 and 7). In larger specimens the stomach and caecum are located in the posterior portion of the mantle, and the esophagus and intestine continue side by side for a considerable distance before joining in the relatively short vestibule. The major portion of the stomach is extremely thin walled and transparent. Posteriorly, it is joined to the tip of the gladius by a slender tissue connection (the 'gastrogenital ligament' of Chun [1910]). The extent of the stomach increases with the size of the animal, so that in **larger** specimens it extends into the tip of the gladius between the vanes, slightly past the midpoint of the fins. In small specimens it terminates at about the level where the vanes begin to form.

The caecum is very small in comparison with that of other teuthoids, with no posterior chamber to increase capacity. As the squid increases in size, the vestibule and stomach become progressively larger, but the size of the caecum increases at a slower rate, so that it becomes proportionally smaller. Its depth is less than the diameter, so that it has a thick button shape. The connection with the vestibule is narrow in comparison with the diameter of the organ. Its spiral nature is readily apparent from the outside.

The intestine leaves the vestibule anteriorly and continues parallel to the esophagus for some distance; then it turns ventrally along the posterior surface of the liver. In its initial portion it is a thick-walled vessel, while the midportion is thin walled and flaccid, with an enlarged diameter. The rectum, which is partially embedded in the distal posterior surface of the liver, becomes thick walled and semi-rigid near the anus. It turns anteriorly at the distal end of the liver, projecting free for some distance in younger specimens but ending at the apex in large ones. The anus is equipped with symmetrical leaflike anal flaps.

The liver is located only slightly anterior to the mantle midpoint in small specimens, but it becomes relatively closer to the head as the mantle lengthens with growth. It is a spindle-shaped organ, larger dorsally and somewhat pointed distally, equal in length to about half the depth of the mantle. It is covered

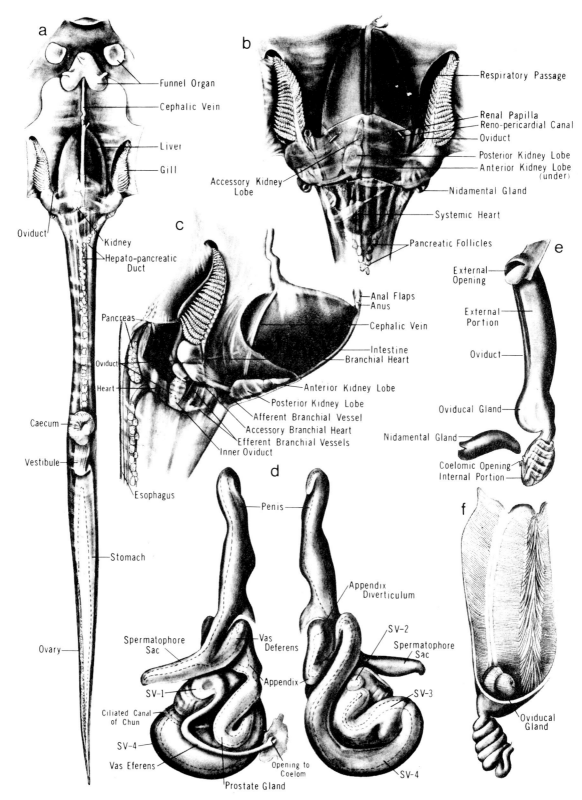

Fig. 6. *Galiteuthis glacialis*, anatomy. (*a*) Viscera, ventral view. (*b*) Anterior viscera, ventral view. (*c*) Same, from left side. (*d*) Male reproductive apparatus. SV is the seminal vesicle. (*e*) Female reproductive apparatus. (*f*) Oviduct, opened to show internal arrangement. (*a*)–(*c*) ELT 1112, female, 395-mm ML. (*d*) ELT 951, male, 231-mm ML. (*e*)–(*f*) ELT 943, female, 286-mm ML.

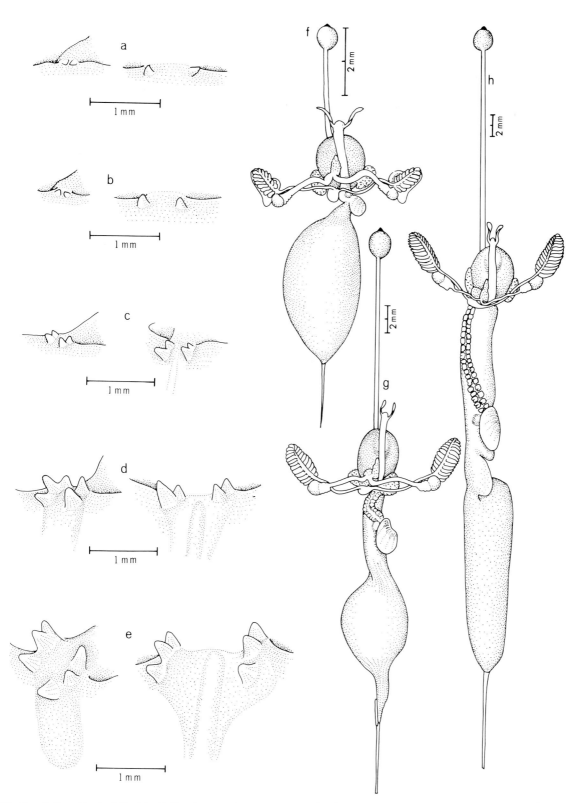

Fig. 7.   *Galiteuthis glacialis.* (*a*)–(*e*) Developmental series of ventral (left) and dorsal (right) mantle fusion tubercles. (*a*) ELT 396, 7-mm ML. (*b*) ELT 918, 9.5-mm ML. (*c*) ELT 949, 16-mm ML. (*d*) ELT 1072, 24-mm ML. (*e*) SC 139, 55-mm ML. (*f*)–(*h*) Series showing proportional change of visceral mass with growth. (*f*) ELT 1077, 14-mm ML. (*g*) SC 139, 55-mm ML. (*h*) ELT 2168, 87-mm ML.

externally with a fragile sheath of highly reflective connective tissue which gives the organ a golden sheen. The paired hepatic ducts exit on the posterolateral surface near the dorsal end.

The pancreas is in three distinct parts, the two anterior portions forming discrete organs and the remainder being semidiffuse. The paired anterior lobes consist of a compound cluster of follicles adjacent to the point where each hepatic duct leaves the liver. The follicles form a central duct connecting with the hepatic duct very close to its exit from the liver sheath. The combined hepatopancreatic duct has a large lumen with a very large connection with the pancreatic duct, so that the follicles are almost in open connection with the duct. The right and left ducts pass posteriorly from the liver around the intestine, joining to form a single duct which follows closely along the intestine to empty into the dorsal side of the caecum anterior to its connection with the vestibule. The remainder of the pancreatic tissue is spread along the length of the hepatopancreatic duct as small clusters of follicles which empty independently into the duct. All the pancreatic tissue has an opaque white color and a very distinctive, mulberrylike appearance.

The ink sac is embedded in the ventral tip of the liver, with the posterior surface partially exposed. It contains longitudinal chambers which join distally to form a duct. The duct parallels the rectum for a short distance, emptying into it just before the anus.

Circulatory system. The systemic heart is located near the middle of the posterior surface of the liver (Figure 6b). It is a slender, muscular, asymmetrical organ, lying over the kidney slightly above the anterior pancreatic lobes. Its position is slightly diagonal to the axis of the liver, with the dorsal end pushed to the right by the esophagus and the ventral end bent somewhat to the left. At its dorsal extremity it gives off the cephalic artery, which in its proximal portion is a thickened, muscular tube separated by a slight constriction from the heart and which curves up to the dorsal end of the liver. Near the middle of the anterior aorta an artery separates which parallels the esophagus and serves the stomach, caecum, and gonad. Near the dorsal end of the liver the cephalic artery is reduced to a slender vessel of constant diameter. Within a short distance it gives off a branch which passes to the dorsal mantle wall with the mesenteries attaching the liver. Here it bifurcates as the posterior mantle arteries, sending a branch posteriorly on either side of the

mantle nerve trunks just under the gladius. At intervals these send branches laterally into the mantle. Directly dorsal to the liver, the cephalic artery gives off the hepatic artery, which passes straight downward into that organ. The cephalic artery continues anteriorly from the liver, passing with the esophagus to the posterior portion of the brain, where it forms a small sinus dorsal and lateral to the esophagus and breaks up into small branches.

The ventral end of the systemic heart is constricted in a small lobe which is displaced slightly to the left. This lobe receives the left efferent branchial vessel at its extremity. The right efferent branchial vessel enters the main sinus of the heart just above the distal lobe. From the base of the lobe, another vessel is given off, which passes under the anterior lobe of the kidney onto the surface of the liver. Here it branches, one branch ramifying over the surface of the liver and supplying the ink sac. The other branch passes under the cephalic vein onto the dorsal wall of the exhalant chamber, then into the lateral mantle wall.

The kidney is a two-lobed organ situated on the posterior surface of the liver capsule, above the middle, and lying on the right side of the intestine (Figure 6b). The anterior lobe is larger, rounded, and slightly bilobed ventrally and drawn out dorsally into two thin-walled sinuses. These pass up the posterior surface of the liver, closely applied to the liver capsule. They communicate widely with the liver around the emerging hepatic ducts and to a lesser extent with the pancreatic lobes. The lateral mantle veins appear to empty into the sinuses at this level. Dorsally, the right vessel joins the posterior mantle artery and parallels its course into the posterior mantle. The course of the left vessel beyond the level of the hepatic ducts is unclear, but it may receive blood from the stomach, caecum, and gonad.

The posterior lobe is situated directly behind the anterior lobe, covering most of its ventral portion. It is constricted ventrally, where it is produced in a small accessory lobe whose lumen is continuous with that of the main portion. Posteriorly, it is wider, and from the lateral corners the afferent branchial vessels lead into the branchial hearts. The cephalic vein connects both anterior and posterior lobes in a common sinus.

The cephalic vein originates in the optic and buccal sinuses. The optic sinuses join in a single median vessel between the optic lobes. The vein pierces the cephalic cartilage at the anterior margin of the statocysts, then passes posteriorly along its ventral surface. It projects through the dorsal funnel wall between the limbs of the dorsal funnel organ member and continues posteriorly, suspended from the dorsal wall of the exhalant chamber, along the midline to the liver. The vessel passes around the right side of the liver and joins the anterior side of the kidney at the junction of the anterior and posterior lobes.

The afferent branchial vessels extend dorsolaterally from the dorsal extremities of the posterior kidney lobe to the branchial hearts at the base of the gills. They are thin-walled vessels that are large in diameter, bearing renal appendages in their proximal portion. They enter the branchial hearts directly through a large opening protected by a membranous funnel-shaped valve. The accessory branchial heart is located immediately posterior to this junction and has a common connection with the afferent vessel and branchial heart. The afferent branchial vessel exits the branchial heart laterally, from a point directly opposite its entrance, and proceeds out the gill.

Nervous system.   Only a few of the major nerves were traced for a portion of their length in serial sections. Some were checked by dissection. The mantle and fin nerves are easily visible in situ with transmitted light.

The branchial nerves originate laterally from the branchial lobe of the brain and proceed anteriorly along the ventral surface of the buccal mass, passing upward laterally at the base of the arms to continue out the center of each arm and tentacle.

The anterior funnel nerves leave the midsubesophageal mass directly below the optic stalks and proceed anteriorly for a short distance along the ventral surface of the mass. They penetrate the cephalic cartilage with the cephalic vein at the anterior margin of the statocysts. The nerves then proceed anteriorly in the dorsal funnel wall, branching laterally. The posterior funnel nerve originates in the posterior subesophageal mass and passes ventrally into the dorsal wall of the wide part of the funnel, contained within the mantle.

The visceral nerves arise from the posterior extremity of the posterior subesophageal mass. They pass downward, proceeding posteriorly along the dorsal funnel wall. They join the cephalic vein behind the funnel organ to continue to the visceral mass.

The pallial nerves originate posterodorsally on the subesophageal mass and proceed almost directly upward along the connective tissue surrounding the esophagus and posterior salivary glands to enter the stellate ganglion. No fibers appear to leave the pallial nerve between the brain and the stellate ganglion. The latter is located just beneath the dorsal mantle wall and lateral to the shell sac, directly behind the nuchal tubercles. Each stellate ganglion gives off four large nerves laterally, which branch and radiate over the anterior half of the mantle. A large posterior mantle and fin nerve trunk leaves each stellate ganglion posteriorly, proceeding close under the gladius to the fin. In the posterior half of the mantle, nerves are given off into the mantle wall.

Reproductive system.   The gonad is a single median organ lying almost entirely on the posterodorsal wall of the stomach and extending a short distance beyond the stomach on the upper branch of the gastrogenital ligament. Sex can be determined in female specimens of less than 15-mm ML by the development of the ovary and in males of about 20 mm with the appearance of the spermatophore apparatus. The testis develops later than the ovary and is not readily visible in specimens of less than 30-mm ML. The sex products of both sexes are shed into the visceropericardial coelom, from which they are removed by the ciliated gonoducts, which open near the base of the left gill in males and near both gills in females.

The ovary (Figure 6a) has a broad, flattened, oval shape and extends partially around the lateral walls of the stomach in larger specimens. As the stomach extends farther posteriorly with growth, the ovary increases proportionally, always extending a little beyond the stomach. In large specimens it extends to about the midpoint of the fins. In preserved material it is brownish, and the individual ova are normally visible under the dissecting microscope.

The paired oviducts (Figures 6f and 6g) lie in the wall of the most lateral extensions of the coelom, across the dorsal surfaces of the branchial hearts and accessory branchial hearts. As in other squids they are composed of three portions, the relative proportions of which are quite different from descriptions in the literature [Williams, 1908; Young and Roper, 1967]. The terminology applied to these parts is modified from the work by Williams [1908].

The inner portion of the oviduct (the 'internal oviduct' of Williams [1908]) is a thin-walled tube, tightly coiled in a flattened spoon-shaped projection above the inner dorsal side of the accessory branchial heart. It connects with the coelom through a U-shaped slitlike opening on the dorsal edge of the projection. This projection comprises about one fifth of the total length of the organ.

The oviducal gland is a very short, straight continuation of the inner portion of the oviduct, with thick walls in the shape of a truncated cone. Around the base of the cone lies a doughnut-shaped ring of spongy glandular tissue. The distal portion of the cone projects free from this ring of tissue and bears longitudinal striae, or lamellae, on its outer surface.

The outer portion of the oviduct (the 'external oviduct' of Williams) comprises about three quarters of the total length of the oviduct. It commences in a hemispherical chamber which covers the protruding duct of the oviducal gland, and it fuses to the circumference of the spongy ring. It continues in a broad, straight tube, oval in cross section, to its opening in the exhalant chamber, at the anterior base of the gill.

The horn-shaped nidamental gland is situated directly below the inner portion of the oviduct, on the posterior side of the accessory branchial heart.

The testis is longer and more slender than the ovary, slightly oval in cross section and attenuate at both ends. It differs greatly in appearance from the ovary, being milky white or light tan in preservation, very fine textured, and much less transparent. In the largest intact specimen examined, it terminated ahead of the fins, while in a female specimen of the same size the ovary extended one quarter of the fin length beyond the leading edge. Although it is not readily apparent at mantle lengths of less than 30 mm, the testis can be seen by careful examination of smaller specimens as a small oval swelling on the upper branch of the gastrogenital ligament, at the posterior tip of the stomach.

The spermatophore apparatus (Figures 6d and 6e) is single, situated on the left side at the base of the gill. It can be identified in specimens of about 30-mm ML but in smaller animals cannot be distinguished from a developing oviduct. At this stage it appears as a short, simple, thick-walled tube, with the diameter nearly equal to the length. The genital sac lies on the anterodorsal surface of the branchial heart, while the penis and appendix project anteriorly along the inner side of the branchial gland. The form of the apparatus is very similar to that described for other oegopsids by Marchand [1907], the differences being in proportion rather than in structure. The extent to which these differences depend on maturity cannot be determined, as no mature males were seen. The apparatus is very small in comparison with that of other teuthoids and in general aspect is extremely compact.

No spermatophores were present in the material examined, and therefore they must remain undescribed. The single mature female specimen seen had numerous sperm reservoirs embedded in the anterior dorsal mantle. These reservoirs measured approximately 0.30 mm in width and up to 27 mm in length. However, this should not be taken as an accurate indication of spermatophore size.

Growth and Development

The fragile nature of cranchiid squids requires that an abundant material be available for a study of the changes produced by growth. The *Eltanin* material meets this requirement, although a large proportion of the animals were severely damaged. In addition to sustaining damage in capture, cranchiid squids are often adversely affected by preservation. Great care is required to prevent severe contraction of the mantle, which causes the gladius to collapse in accordionlike folds. Accurate mantle lengths can then best be determined by measuring the dissected gladius or by measuring the segments of the gladius through the mantle wall, using transmitted light. The extensive contraction caused by careless preservation also renders other measurements unreliable and distorts the arrangement of the internal anatomy.

Measurements in addition to mantle length were made on all specimens over 80-mm ML, while the large number of specimens below that size necessitated selecting a series for each 10-mm size group which consisted of carefully selected specimens

TABLE 3. Summary of Measurements Made on a Selected Series of *Galiteuthis glacialis*, Representing the Entire Size Range Available

Measurement	Range	Mean	Number of Observations
Mantle length	4.0–496.0	94.2	106
Mantle width	2.0–85.0	13.0	104
Head width	2.4–63.0	14.5	96
Cranial width	0.8–30.0	7.1	101
Eye diameter	0.8–35.0	8.2	96
Fin length	0.2–164.0	32.3	102
Fin width	0.3–75.0	16.1	95
Arm length			
I	0.3–91.0	25.8	80
II	0.4–101.0	29.7	76
III	0.4–105.0	31.2	81
IV	0.2–101.0	29.5	79
Tentacle length	5.0–174.0	68.7	76
Club length	2.2–27.0	8.0	126
Gill length	0.5–14.5	5.3	124

Measurements are in millimeters.

TABLE 4. Range, Mean, and Standard Deviation of Indices of a Selected Series of *Galiteuthis glacialis*, Derived From Measurements Summarized in Table 1

Index	Range	Mean	Standard Deviation	Number of Observations
Mantle width index	12.0–45.5	18.9	4.90	104
Fin length index	2.9–44.0	26.9	9.77	102
Fin width index	6.1–21.6	14.2	2.84	95
Fin length/fin width	28.6–212.5	58.3	24.04	95
Head width index				
Total	12.0–46.6	19.2	6.03	97
Cranial	6.0–16.6	8.0	1.61	103
Arm length index				
I	7.8–23.8	14.5	4.21	40
II	10.7–27.2	18.0	3.63	40
III	14.1–29.0	19.9	3.08	40
IV	14.6–27.7	20.0	3.00	40
Tentacle length index	30.6–60.7	50.3	6.72	37
Club length index	5.9–13.3	8.2	1.55	91
Gill length index	4.1–12.2	7.1	1.66	97

Measurements are in millimeters.

showing minimum distortion. The number in each varied, but an attempt was made to measure at least ten individuals in every size group. The number of observations of each character often varies from the total number of animals measured, owing to partial damage or distortion of some individuals. Some counts and measurements could not be made with reasonable accuracy on small individuals. These are discussed further below.

The range and mean of measurements made on selected specimens of *G. glacialis* are given in Table 3. Meristic observations are summarized in Table 5. Individual observations are plotted against mantle length in Figures 9–11 and 13. Because of the physical limitations of the graphs it was not possible to plot every observation, but as many were plotted as was possible without confusion. The plots include the extremes noted in the measurements.

All values plotted are obviously isometric, showing that relative proportions change very little above 20-mm ML. Most of the apparent changes in form take place below this size, but few measurements can be made with sufficient accuracy to show this. Such changes are discussed below. The graphs accentuate

the fact that there is little or no external difference in the sexes.

Some measurements and counts were not made below 70- to 80-mm ML, except on specimens in exceptionally good condition. The arms are very attenuate distally and most often are tightly curled from preservation. Obtaining accurate measurements of arm length or sucker counts is nearly impossible in small specimens unless they are perfectly preserved, since introduced error becomes unacceptably large. Tentacular carpal, manal, and dactylar suckers are indistinguishable in smaller specimens. The eyes are round in large specimens, but below about 100-mm ML the eyes are oval, and the measurement plotted represents the major diameter. This is discussed below. Other measurements and counts were made throughout the size range.

Changes with growth. Some of the morphological and anatomical changes which the species undergoes with growth cannot be expressed clearly by measurements alone. The measurements have been converted to indices (proportion of mantle length), which are summarized in Table 4. Range, mean, and

TABLE 5. Summary of Counts of Tentacular Stalk Suckers and Gill Filaments Made on a Selected Series of *Galiteuthis glacialis*

Tentacular stalk suckers*																			
Number of suckers	45	47	48	49	50	51	52	53	54	55	56	57	58	59	60	62	64	68	72
Number of observations	1	3	1	8	12	11	14	1	18	13	12	5	4	1	5	8	2	2	2
Gill filaments†																			
Number of filaments	7	10	11	12	13	14	15	16	17	18	19	20	21	22	23	24	26		
Number of observations	1	2	1	2	2	6	6	6	13	18	20	13	7	13	9	7	1		

Values not observed are omitted.

*For the tentacular stalk sucker count, 123 specimens were examined.

†For the gill filament count, 127 specimens were examined.

standard deviation are given for each index. The general changes in form of various portions of the anatomy will be discussed briefly, while some aspects, including those of taxonomic importance, will be treated in more detail.

The shape of the mantle is greatly affected by the condition of the animal when it is preserved. Smaller specimens often inflate the mantle with water until it attains a nearly spherical shape, and this may persist in preservation. When the water is forced out, an animal which has been preserved in this state retains the appearance of a deflated balloon. The other extreme also occurs, when a specimen preserved in a greatly contracted state has an elongate, slender appearance. The majority of individuals have a teardrop shape, widest in the anterior third of the mantle and attenuate posteriorly (Figure 8). Because of the extreme variability, no attempt was made to measure the mantle width in the midportion, but it can be seen from Figure 9a that the anterior width is a fairly constant proportion of a given mantle length. This proportion becomes very gradually smaller above 20-mm ML, with a MWI of about 12.0–14.0 in very large specimens. Very small specimens, below 15-mm ML, have a more saccular mantle, with a MWI of 30.0–50.0.

The scattered mantle tubercules first become visible in histological sections from specimens of slightly less that 100-mm ML. They can be seen under the dissecting microscope in specimens slightly larger and with the naked eye at about 125-mm ML. They first appear as thickenings in the outer mantle layer, composed of what appears to be connective tissue. This is gradually replaced by cartilage, commencing in the outer layers, until they are solid cylinders, embedded in the spongy layer and projecting slightly through the outer layer.

The tubercles at the dorsal fusion point first appear at about 5- to 6-mm ML, as small dots. The ventral tubercles, on the funnel-mantle fusion, appear at about 7 mm, slightly lateral to the actual fusion point. The dorsal tubercles develop very slowly, first having a conical shape and then developing additional points at the anterior margin, acquiring a second point at about 10–12 mm and a third at about 25 mm. They then remain in essentially this condition throughout the life of the animal. In larger specimens the thicker mantle partially overgrows the tubercles, making them difficult to detect. The ventral tubercles develop faster than the dorsal ones, adding a second point on the inner side of the first,

directly over the fusion with the funnel, at about 9-mm ML. Both points then acquire additional points at the anterior margin, until by a mantle length of about 18 mm there are three points forming an outer row and two forming an inner row. Both rows gain at least one additional point, and large specimens may have five points in the outer row and four in the inner.

The fins are extremely small in the smallest specimens seen and are widely separated, with their position influenced by the developing gladius (see discussion of gladius development below). Below 10-mm ML they have very short bases which diverge anteriorly at about a 45° angle, and width is greater than length. With growth the angle between the fin insertions becomes smaller. In large specimens they are nearly parallel and diverge only slightly in the anterior portion. The fins elongate with growth and are semicircular at 20- to 25-mm ML. Above this size the greatest width is in the anterior portion, although a free lobe is never present. In large specimens the fin is quite attenuate posteriorly (Figure 1).

The changes which the head exhibits in the course of development (Figure 10) are almost entirely the result of changes in the eyes, which are discussed below. The anterior cranial portion, which has a rectangular cross section even below 10-mm ML, projects somewhat in smaller specimens but never gives the brachial crown a stalked appearance as in some other cranchiid genera. The projecting condition disappears as the eyes become sessile.

The eyes of small specimens are usually distorted, making their shape uncertain in the smallest individuals. They are borne on short, thick stalks having a diameter greater than that of the visual elements, and they project downward and laterally. The stalks appear to be filled with fluid and are greatly affected by preservation. No attempt was made to measure their length, but the eye appears to comprise at least half of the entire structure, even at the greatest stalk development. Above about 15-mm ML the eye occupies more than half of the stalk, while the optic lobe occupies the rest. The plane of the lateral surface of the eye is parallel to the sagittal plane and makes an angle with the stalk. The eye appears to be round in some of the smallest specimens, but this may be the effect of preservation. It is clearly oval in well-preserved specimens above about 10-mm ML, with the major axis vertical. There is never any trace of a 'rostrum' developed ventrally. The oval shape persists until about 100-mm ML, when the eye becomes round. The eyes become sessile much earlier, at about 50-mm ML, and eventually occupy the entire lateral surface of the cranial portion, covering the bases of the arms.

The large photophore (Figure 1c) first appears between 20- and 25-mm ML. The marginal rim starts to thicken at about 50-mm ML, while the smaller organ first appears at about 50- to 55-mm ML. The larger organ appears to have its definitive form at about 75-mm ML, while the smaller organ does not achieve this state until about 125-mm ML. In larger specimens the smaller organ loses its crescent shape and becomes straight and bar-shaped.

The olfactory organ (Figure 3f) is first visible externally at about 40-mm ML as a small circular thickening on the middle of the posterior surface of the eye, just behind the margin of the large photophore. With growth the central portion becomes depressed, giving it a cup-shaped appearance, while the entire organ becomes elongate, forming a stalk which protrudes perpendicularly from the surface of the eye. Between 75- and 100-mm ML the stalk becomes slightly constricted in the proximal portion. Even in large individuals the length of the organ is no more than twice the diameter. The nerve and blood vessels which serve this organ run a short distance over the eye, just under the epithelial layer, before penetrating the capsule. When the supporting skin is torn away, the organ remains attached by these vessels, giving the impression of being on a long, slender stalk.

The funnel is proportionally quite large in the smallest specimens. At 5-mm ML it covers the entire ventral surface of the head and part of the eyestalks and projects anteriorly to the rudiments of the ventral arms. At this stage it points anteriorly and does not show the ventral flexion that is characteristic of larger individuals. The rest of the head portion appears to grow more rapidly, since the funnel becomes proportionally shorter and narrower in larger individuals. The ventral flexion develops early, the dorsal funnel wall turning ventrally at 9- to 10-mm ML and the ventral wall developing a valvelike fold at 12- to 15-mm ML.

The two dorsal pairs of arms develop at about the same rate, slightly faster than the two ventral pairs. The second pair is slightly longer, and both dorsal pairs are thick and blunt in the earliest stages. In the smallest specimen available (slightly less than 4-mm ML) the two dorsal pairs of arms were less than 0.2

mm long, with 2-4 suckers each. The two ventral pairs showed only as tiny protuberances without suckers. At slightly over 4-mm ML the ventral arms have 2-4 suckers but are still insignificantly small in comparison with the dorsal pairs. At a mantle length of 9 mm the second pair of arms is still longest, although the third pair has an equal number of suckers (about 12). Both ventral pairs, although approaching the dorsal pairs in length, are very slender, with a diameter that is only about half that of the dorsal pairs. At 15-mm ML the arm formula is $3 > 2 > 1 = 4$, the three ventral pairs all having about the same number of suckers (12-14). Between 25- and 35-mm ML the arms attain the formula $4 = 3 > 2 > 1$, which is maintained with some exceptions throughout the size range seen (Figure 11). At this size they have an approximately equal diameter. Above an undetermined mantle length (30-50 mm) the ventral arms actually become distinctly longer than the third pair, but this is masked by the method of measurement. Measurements must be made from the proximal sucker for lack of any other reliable landmark, and the suckers of the ventral arms start some distance from the base of the arm. Dentition of the suckers consists of very few irregular incisions in the young animals and progresses gradually to more regular, blunt teeth. Regular, pointed teeth develop only in the distal sucker rings of larger individuals. Protective membranes and keels develop in small individuals (less than 50-mm ML) but are very easily damaged and often lost. In addition, shrinkage in preservation often obscures the structures, so the complete progression of development could not be determined.

The tentacles were strongly developed in the earliest stages seen. The length is variable, depending on preservation and condition of the specimen. Between 4- and 7-mm ML, tentacle length appears to be about equal to mantle length and sometimes slightly exceeds it. At 10-mm ML the tentacles are definitely shorter than the mantle, and this condition exists in all larger specimens. In large individuals the tentacle length varies widely according to the state of contraction, but in general, the length is about half the mantle length. In this study the protective membranes were considered to delineate the club portion. They are first distinguishable at about 20-mm ML, and by 30 mm there is a well-delineated club with four rows of suckers, while the two rows of stalk suckers are slightly smaller (see Figure 12). The transition between the two is gradual, and the limit

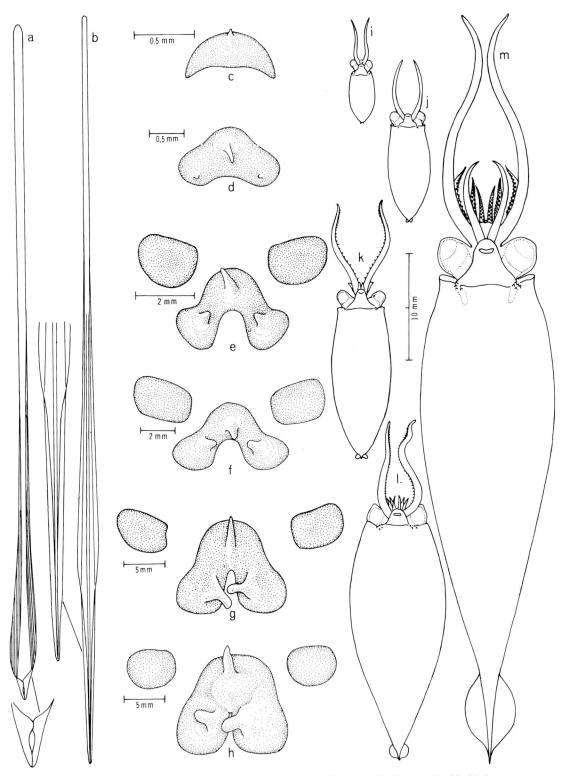

Fig. 8. *Galiteuthis glacialis.* (*a*), (*b*) Gladius. (*a*) ELT 1970, 18-mm ML. (*b*) ELT 1665, 65-mm ML. (*c*)–(*h*) Funnel organ growth series. (*c*) ELT 302, 7-mm ML. (*d*) ELT 949, 16-mm ML. (*e*) ELT 949, 51-mm ML. (*f*) ELT 1071, 115-mm ML. (*g*) ELT 943, 286-mm ML. (*h*) ELT H-371, 297-mm ML. (*i*)–(*m*) Change of proportion with growth. (*i*) ELT 302, 5-mm ML. (*j*) ELT 1050, 10-mm ML. (*k*) ELT 949, 16-mm ML. (*l*) ELT 1072, 24-mm ML. (*m*) ELT 949, 51-mm ML. (*i*)–(*m*) To same scale.

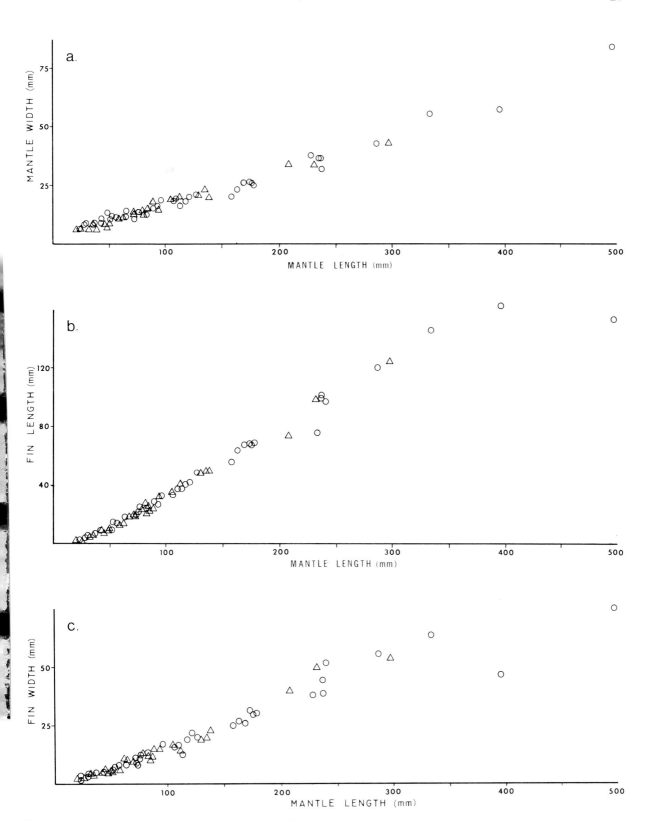

Fig. 9. *Galiteuthis glacialis*, morphometric relationships. Standard measurements compared to mantle length. (*a*) Mantle width. (*b*) Fin length. (*c*) Fin width. Triangles represent males, circles females.

imposed by the protective membrane is somewhat arbitrary. A clear carpal cluster does not develop until after hooks have developed. It first becomes distinct above 75-mm ML. The position of the first hook to develop is somewhat variable, but it is in the second or third pair of the adult series. It appears at a mantle length of 55–65 mm. The hooks form by a gradual fusion and enlargement of the median distal teeth of the chitinous ring (Figures 4c–4g), which, as they enlarge, incorporate the lateral teeth. The ring aperture becomes smaller as the hooks develop, until finally it is reduced to a small pore. The basal portion of the chitinous ring flattens and develops digitate projections on either side. The hooks form both proximally and distally from the first one, although most develop distally. The carpal apparatus becomes distinct before the most proximal hooks are formed, and a clear transformation of the distal carpal sucker into a hook has been seen. The number of hooks is somewhat variable, and the maximum attainable number is unknown. The maximum number encountered was 12, in a male of only 207-mm ML. Most females had only 10 or occasionally 11. Many large specimens were missing tentacles or hooks, so some uncertainty in this respect must remain. In those large individuals with intact tentacles it appears that no more hooks will form distally, as there is a tremendous size discrepancy between the distal hook and the proximal dactylar sucker. All other hooks appear to form before the preceding hook has enlarged much. Whether hooks continue to form proximally from carpal suckers throughout the life of the animal is unknown, but it appears that 12 may be a maximum number. Stalk suckers are borne on elongate peduncles in small individuals, but these become relatively shorter as the animal increases in size. In large individuals the suckers are attached by very short, slender peduncles and are partially recessed in the oral face of the tentacular stalk. Protective membranes never become very broad and never develop the prominent trabeculae characteristic of some cranchiids, although weak trabeculae are present. The dorsal keel is discernible at less than 50-mm ML, but even in large individuals it is only a minute flap. Figure 13 illustrates the relationship between club length and mantle length. Variation in the number of stalk suckers is shown in Table 5.

The gladius is membranous and transparent in small specimens, with the posterior portion expanded in broad vanes. The posterior tip is thickened and pointed, forming a minute point between the vanes, which are broadest at the posterior margin. At less than 100-mm ML the vanes curl under posterolaterally to form a broad, shallow pseudoconus. The fins insert transversely over the vanes, and the angle between the fin insertions is determined by the amount that the vanes are curled under. With growth the tip of the gladius elongates posteriorly, and the vanes turn under closer to the ventral midline. This causes an elongation of the pseudoconus formed and decreases the angle between the fin insertions. By 20-mm ML (Figure 8a) the vanes overlap ventrally, while the dorsal portion of the gladius has become thick and strong. The posterior tip of the gladius is still broad at this size, but by 25-mm ML it has narrowed considerably, and the angle between the fin insertions is very small. The gladius retains this conformation at larger sizes, becoming thicker but proportionally narrower with increased length. The rachis remains slender, thin, and flexible at all sizes examined. It maintains a constant width to the extreme anterior tip.

Except in the smallest sizes, development of the mandibles consists mostly of thickening and additional pigmentation. In the smaller individuals, only the rostral tip of either mandible has color. At less than 15-mm ML the rostrum and shoulder of the mandibles bear a layer of transparent cartilaginous material which forms a somewhat irregular, semicircular cutting edge. The characteristics of the rostrum and jaw angle can be seen through this material. Above 20-mm ML this accessory cutting edge is lost, and the rostral portion of the mandibles is darkened as far back as the jaw angle. At 35-mm ML the mandibles have all the characteristics seen in the largest specimens, with the exception that the dark pigmentation only covers the hood and shoulders. Faint coloration extends past the wings in the crest and lateral wall. At this size the projections arming the anterior shoulder below the jaw angle are extremely prominent. With increased size the projections appear to be gradually incorporated into the lateral wall, so that they become less prominent. However, they were still apparent in both mandibles at the largest size examined. By 250-mm ML, both mandibles are entirely pigmented, except for the posterior margins where chitin is added, the intensity of pigmentation decreasing posteriorly. The tip of the rostrum becomes completely opaque at an early stage, and the opacity gradually progresses

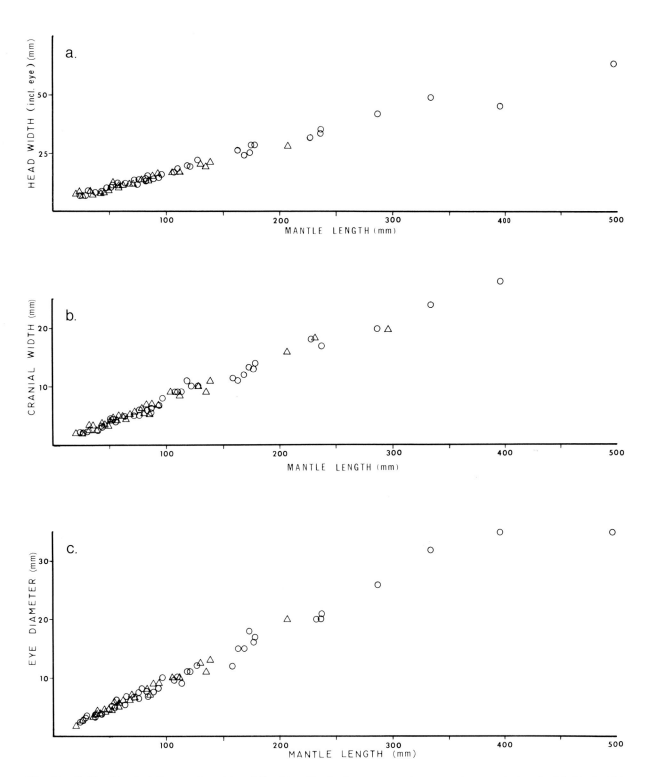

Fig. 10. *Galiteuthis glacialis*, morphometric relationships. Standard measurements compared to mantle length. (*a*) Head width (including eyes). (*b*) Cranial width. (*c*) Eye diameter. Triangles represent males, circles females.

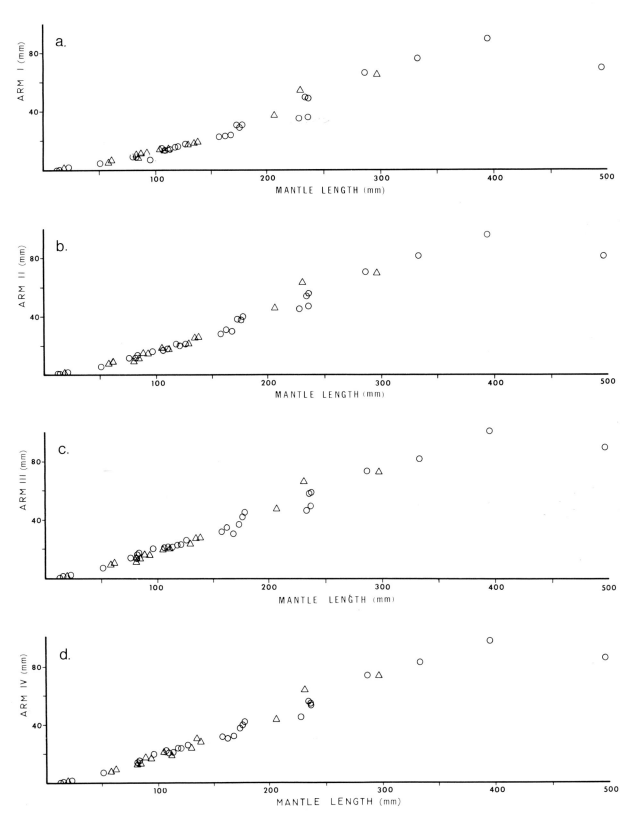

Fig. 11. *Galiteuthis glacialis*, morphometric relationships. Arm length compared to mantle length. Triangles represent males, circles females.

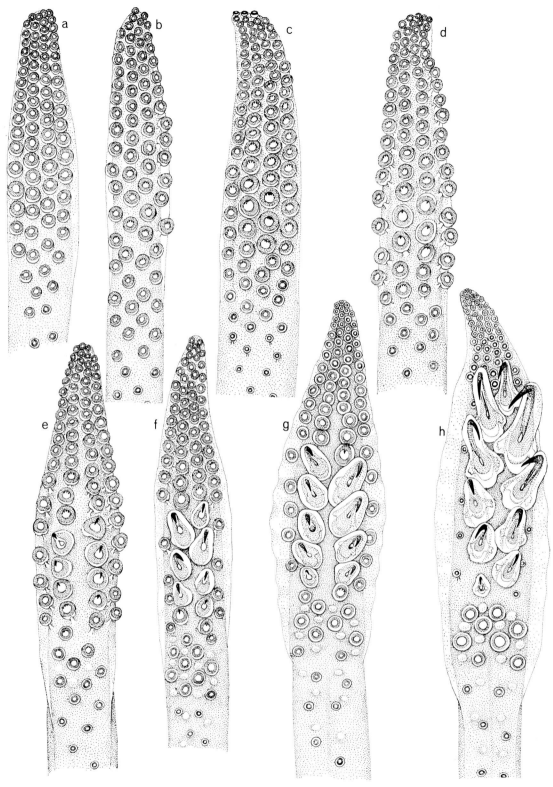

Fig. 12.   *Galiteuthis glacialis.* Developmental series of tentacular clubs. (*a*) Right, ELT 683, 26-mm ML. (*b*) Right, SC 24-62, 38-mm ML. (*c*) Left, ELT 935, 55-mm ML. (*d*) Right, ELT 949, 62-mm ML. (*e*) Left, ELT 949, 84-mm ML. (*f*) Left, ELT 1023, 107-mm ML. (*g*) Left, ELT 1634, 130-mm ML. (*h*) Left, ELT 992, 235-mm ML.

back over the hood and crest. The largest mandibles examined were still transparent amber over most of the crest and lateral wall.

The radula shows less change with growth than the mandibles. The ribbon is formed at an early stage, although it is very thin and fragile. Marginal plates can not be seen in small specimens. With growth the teeth and basal plates become larger and thicker and acquire an amber color, presumably from the additional thickness.

Maturity. Adult stages of cranchiid squids, perhaps to a greater degree than all other oegopsid families, are relatively unknown. The tremendous morphological changes which many species undergo in the course of their development have resulted in confusion in the taxonomic literature, as authors have applied new names to different growth stages [Clarke, 1966; Voss, 1967a]. The principal factor perpetuating this confusion has been the lack of a sufficient material available to any one investigator. Although impressive midwater collections now in existence will probably resolve many of the nomenclatural problems, the adults of many species are still unknown and will remain so until large midwater trawls come into more widespread use.

Some uncertainty has existed concerning the maximum size attained by cranchiids. One antarctic species, *Mesonychoteuthis hamiltoni*, is known to attain a large size [Robson, 1925; Clarke, 1966; K. N. Nesis, personal communication, 1972], and it has not been unreasonable to suppose that other species may also. This supposition is supported by reports of large specimens of *Phasmatopsis cymoctypus* from the Atlantic [de Rochebrune, 1884; Clarke, 1962a]. In the course of this study, *G. glacialis* was compared at various stages with closely related species (i.e., other species of *Galiteuthis* and *Taonius*). Development appeared to proceed at approximately the same rate in these other species, so it may be presumed that they mature at about the same size. This would suggest that *M. hamiltoni* is probably an exception within the family.

The *Eltanin* material contained a single mature specimen of *G. glacialis*, a female of 496-mm ML which was apparently on the verge of spawning. The ovary of this specimen was fragmented during capture, and most eggs were free in the mantle cavity, since the coelomic wall was ruptured. Some eggs were apparently lost through a rupture in the dorsal mantle wall, but the volume of those remaining, with some ovarian fragments, was more than 600 ml. The

eggs were of uniform size and oval shape, ranging from 3.75 to 4.00 mm in length and 2.70 to 2.80 mm in diameter. The eggs in the ovary of the second largest female, with a mantle length of 395 mm, were much smaller, most being about 0.60 mm in length and 0.45 mm in diameter, while the smallest were only about half that size. The eggs which remained in portions of the ovary still in place in the larger specimen were attached by one end to the dorsal midline of the stomach by a slender threadlike tissue connection. These eggs were quite variable in size, as was the case in the smaller female, some being only 1.5 mm long. This variability appears to be due to the crowding of the eggs in the ovary itself rather than to any difference in development and is probably accentuated by shrinkage in preservation.

Clarke [1962a] described a large (810-mm ML) female example of *Phasmatopsis cymoctypus* in which the 'eggs vary in size to a marked degree.' From this variation he deduced differential development leading to continuous maturation. He attributes the same phenomenon to *Taonius*, from a description by Verrill [1881, p. 440], 'some ovules larger than the rest.' In a 296-mm ML specimen of *Taonius* examined during this study the ova ranged from 0.05 to 0.20 mm in diameter, with the majority between 0.16 and 0.20 mm. A female *G. glacialis* of 286-mm ML had ova only slightly larger, with about the same range of variation. It would appear that the eggs hydrate rapidly just before spawning, and size differences largely disappear.

The gravid *G. glacialis* female exhibited a gelatinous condition which appeared to be related to the near-spawning state. The mantle and fins were very soft and fragile, and even the arms were soft, without the hard, muscular consistency exhibited by other specimens. Sections showed that the musculature was greatly reduced, consisting of isolated strands running through a gelatinous matrix (Figure 2c). There was a reticulate network of tissue which appeared to form honeycomblike chambers enclosing the gelatinous material. The cartilaginous tubercles, which are extremely prominent and give the mantle a coarse, sandpaperlike texture in the 395-mm ML female, are reduced to low, rounded, smooth nodules in the large specimen. The general deterioration appears to be the result of the tremendous metabolic expense of producing such a large quantity of eggs. Such deterioration connected with spawning has been noted in other oegopsid squid families [Hamabe, 1963; R. E. Young, personal com-

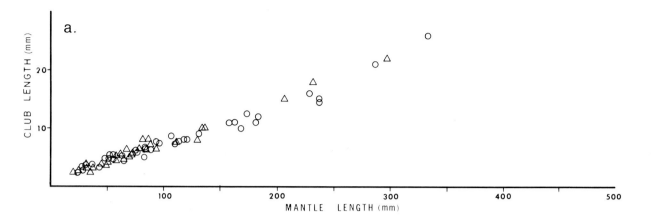

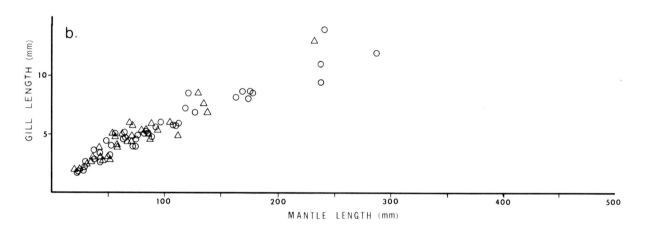

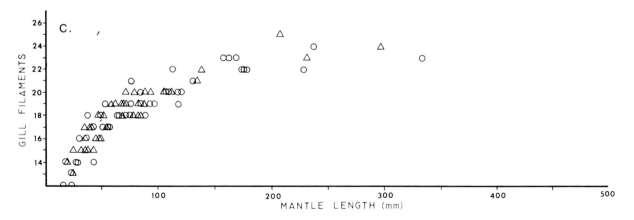

Fig. 13.　*Galiteuthis glacialis*, morphometric relationships. Standard measurements and counts compared to mantle length. (*a*) Tentacular club length. (*b*) Gill length. (*c*) Number of gill filaments (outer demibranch). Triangles represent males, circles females.

munication, 1968]. It seems highly likely that the female of this species dies after spawning.

Clarke [1962a] reported that his specimen of *Phasmatopsis cymoctypus* had a spermatophore capsule 'unattached within the body cavity near the anterior end of the ovary.' He professed wonder at its occurrence here, because 'the body wall seems to be quite intact.' The female specimen described here seems to shed some light on this problem. Numerous (about 24) sperm reservoirs were attached to the dorsal mantle surface near the anterior margin (Figure 2). These measured about 0.30 mm in diameter and up to 27 mm long. All were firmly attached throughout their length, and some were seen to be deeply embedded in the mantle wall. Examination of the internal surface revealed that several of these reservoirs had penetrated the mantle wall and were projecting free into the inhalant chamber. One was almost completely free, with only a millimeter or two of its length still embedded perpendicularly and with only a slight scar marking its passage. It appears that a chemical mechanism exists, possibly enzymatic and probably involving one of the layers of the sperm reservoir tunic, which allows the reservoir to pass through the mantle wall. The breakdown of the muscular elements in the mantle may aid this penetration. If the sperm reservoir penetrates at a position close to the gladius, as one was in the process of doing in this instance, it could easily end up in the coelomic cavity. Fertilization might then take place before the eggs enter the oviduct. This requires rather precise placement of the spermatophore and is probably not the usual sequence of events. If the sperm reservoir enters the inhalant chamber, as several were in the process of doing here, it would move with the respiratory currents through the opening into the exhalant chamber, passing close to the opening of the oviducal gland. Where fertilization normally takes place in this species is unknown. In the Ommastrephidae it has been suggested that it takes place external to the mantle [Hamabe, 1961]. Since the oviducts are located well within the mantle, it is likely that the eggs are fertilized within the mantle in *G. glacialis*; this hypothesis is supported by the penetration of the sperm reservoirs into the mantle. Morphologically, it would appear most likely that fertilization takes place within or immediately after the eggs leave the distal portion of the oviduct. One other question remains unanswered: Are the eggs shed free or enclosed in a gelatinous mass? The latter possibility

seems more likely, and this may involve the nidamental glands, which develop progressively with the oviducts. Both oviducts and nidamental glands are missing from the gravid specimen, so the extent of their development cannot be determined.

The largest male specimen had a mantle length of 297 mm and was clearly immature. It showed no apparent external differences from a female of the same size. There was no sign of spermatophores in the spermatophore sac, and no indication of hectocotylization. It seems unlikely that hectocotylization develops at a later stage, since the largest male appeared to have reached its definitive form and in those species where hectocotylization is known, it develops at an earlier stage. Nothing more can be added to the knowledge of the male at this point.

Miscellaneous Observations on Galiteuthis glacialis

Swimming. Clarke [1962b] described the respiratory and swimming movements of another cranchiid squid, *Cranchia scabra* (Leach). Since the membrane arrangement of all cranchiids is similar, Clarke's observations can be extended to this species.

In *C. scabra*, changes of position were accomplished by fin movements, while the neutrally buoyant animal remained otherwise nearly motionless. Clarke observed only infrequent contractions of the mantle, in conjunction with weak escape movements by the animal, and stated [Clarke, 1962b, p. 352] that the mantle only gradually refilled to recover its globular shape. Respiratory circulation was accomplished entirely by contractions of the walls of the coelomic cavity. Contraction of the anterior portion of the coelom reduced the volume of that chamber within the anterior portion of the mantle, causing water to flow into the inhalant chamber. At the same time, the contraction forced the coelomic fluid into the posterior portion of the coelom, forcing water out of the exhalant chamber. Clarke found the contraction to be wavelike in nature and repeated continuously, creating a constant flow of water through the mantle.

Observations made of *G. glacialis* in running seawater aquaria aboard the U.S.N.S. *Eltanin* show some minor differences from Clarke's comments. The squids normally were quite active, moving about the aquarium much of the time. For long periods, however, they would hang motionless, with the only obvious movements confined to the tentacles and arms. Larger specimens were oriented slightly tail downward, while smaller ones hung slightly head downward. The difference is probably due to a change in center of gravity caused by the heavier development of the posterior part of the gladius and its further removal from the vicinity of the major portion of the coelom, which is responsible for buoyancy [Denton et al., 1969]. Fin movements were observed occasionally, but the slenderness and extreme transparency of the fins in the specimen sizes observed (25–100 mm) made these movements very difficult to detect. Movement might have been continuous but observed only when lighting conditions were correct. Some funnel movements were observed, and small changes of position and minor movements about the tank appeared to have been accomplished with the funnel. The fairly active behavior of the animals compared with the small size of the fin suggests that the funnel plays a significant part in normal locomotion, in contrast to the situation in *C. scabra*. Escape reactions were occasionally observed, apparently much more vigorous than in *C. scabra*. In one instance the squid shot half the length of the aquarium (approximately 30 cm), hitting the end with enough force to cause a permanent bend of about 70° near the middle of the gladius. This apparently caused the squid no serious difficulty, although it hampered movement somewhat. Respiratory movements of the mantle were not observed, although it was noted that a stream of water issued from the funnel more or less steadily.

Stomach contents. Bidder [1966] has stated that cephalopods bite their food into pieces and swallow it in this form, with little or no rasping action from the radula. No observations were made on feeding of live specimens of *G. glacialis*, but examination of stomach contents supports this view, as material found in the stomach of this species was often in surprisingly large, relatively undamaged pieces.

Most individuals had some food remaining in the stomach, while a few had a relatively large quantity of food and some had only indigestible hard parts remaining. *G. glacialis* appears to be an opportunistic feeder, consuming almost any type of organism. Although much of the stomach contents was unidentifiable, many specimens had hard parts which identified the prey organism on a very general scale. The most common items were crustacean exoskeletons. Remains were identified as originating from copepods, amphipods, and euphausids. The next most common item was chaetognath spines, with the

head often relatively intact. Presumably, the density of the head musculature makes it more difficult to digest. Fish remains were encountered occasionally, but by no means commonly. It is possible that much of the unidentifiable material was of fish origin. In one specimen the remains of the cephalic cartilage of a cephalopod, including the statolith, were seen, with some bits of gladius. The stomach of another specimen contained the intact superior nectophore of a small siphonophore. Curious bilateral, apparently chitinous objects having a symmetrical spearhead shape were seen in stomachs of several animals. The identity of these objects was never determined, although in one specimen they appeared to be attached to fragments of a thin, transparent ribbon. This suggested a radular ribbon, but a search of the literature and inquiry among other workers provided no clue to their origin.

No attempt was made to quantify the observations of stomach contents, but the order of preference in food items appeared to be crustacea, chaetognatha, fish, and miscellaneous organisms.

Galiteuthis aspera Filippova

Galiteuthis aspera Filippova, 1972, p. 400, fig. 7.

Discussion. This species was created by Filippova on the basis of four specimens trawled in the Scotia Sea. The description is brief, but adequate, and there can be no doubt that these are specimens of *G. glacialis*.

Although her description differs in two characters from that given here, Filippova mentions the two primary distinguishing characters of *G. glacialis*: the presence of complex tubercles at both funnel and nuchal mantle fusion points and the cartilaginous tubercles on the mantle surface. She states [Filippova, 1972, p. 400], 'On the surface of the mantle, at the points of its attachment with the funnel and the head, there are clusters of 5–6 spines.' This statement is somewhat confusing with respect to the dorsal tubercles, but her illustration clearly shows two points on either side of the gladius. These complex tubercles at the dorsal fusion distinguish *G. glacialis* from all other cranchiids. Cartilaginous tubercles on the surface of the mantle is a condition which has not been seen in any other antarctic cranchiid.

Filippova's description differs first in the FLI, which ranged from 43 to 50. This index increases with specimen size, but none of the *Eltanin* specimens had an FLI greater than 44. FLI, perhaps more than other indices, tends to increase as a result of contraction of the mantle in preservation. This is due to the heavy, rigid posterior portion of the gladius, which prevents distortion of that part of the mantle (and fins).

The second difference occurs in the arm formula, given by Filippova as $3 > 2 > 4 > 1$ and presented in this paper as $4 = 3 > 2 > 1$. This feature was found in the present study to be quite variable, changing with age and often differing from specimen to specimen. In the *Eltanin* material the third arms tended to be longest in specimens of greater than 150-mm ML, while the fourth arms were usually longest in specimens between 50- and 150-mm ML. However, exceptions occurred in both cases. At all mantle lengths the second and fourth arms were very close in length. It was interesting to note that variation between arms of the same pair was often equal to or greater than that between pairs. The formula of $4 = 3 > 2 > 1$ given here represents the most common condition and is of limited taxonomic value.

Of greater interest than the arm formula are the absolute arm lengths given by Filippova. The arm lengths of the smallest paratype correspond closely to *Eltanin* material of equal mantle length. The holotype arm measurements are about 20% shorter than in *Eltanin* specimens of equal mantle lengths, while the two larger paratypes are drastically shorter. Although not mentioned by the author, this condition would appear to represent loss of some portion of the arm tips (not uncommon), as the arm indices of these specimens are smaller than in any described cranchiid.

In all other respects, Filippova's description corresponds closely to *Eltanin* material of *G. glacialis*, and the differences discussed here are considered within the range of specific variation.

Comparison With Galiteuthis beringiana (Sasaki)

Galiteuthis beringiana (Sasaki, 1920)

Crystalloteuthis beringiana Sasaki, 1920, p. 202, pl. 26, fig. 4; Clarke, 1966, p. 217.
Crystalloteuthis behringiana Sasaki, 1929, p. 324, pl. 25, figs. 10–15, text-fig. 149; Kondakov, 1941; Akimushkin, 1963, p. 197.

Location of type specimen. U.S. National Museum. Holotype, female, USNM 332921;

paratypes, USNM 332919, 332920, 332922, and 332923.

Discussion. Sasaki's type material was examined during this study for purposes of generic and specific comparison. Sasaki's original description is sufficiently detailed for the present purposes, so the material will not be redescribed. While a complete description of the species requires a more complete series, the material is in good condition and shows several noteworthy features. External and internal characteristics show that these are clearly juveniles of *Galiteuthis*, and a treatment of the genus on a worldwide basis will require further study of these specimens. The species is similar in several respects to *Galiteuthis phyllura* Berry (1911), which occurs off the northern California coast, and Nesis [1972] has suggested that they are conspecific. Unfortunately, the California material available consisted of individuals much larger than Sasaki's largest specimen, comparison thus being made difficult. *Galiteuthis glacialis* and *G. beringiana* are readily separable on the basis of external characters alone, but because they have been related in the literature, all major points of difference are discussed here. All comparisons are made at equivalent mantle lengths.

The complex tubercles at the dorsal mantle fusion separate *G. glacialis* from all other described cranchiids. The remainder of the external differences between the two are mostly a matter of degree. The mantle and fins have virtually identical dimensions and shape. The head is similar in both, but the eyes are very different. The eyestalks of *G. glacialis* are very thick and almost completely occupied by the optic lobe. The optic nerve is little more than a slender constriction between the brain and the optic lobe. The eye is quite large. At the same mantle length the eyestalk of *G. beringiana* is nearly identical in length but has only half the diameter. The optic lobe is small, occupying only the distal half of the stalk, while the optic nerve is longer than the proximal half of the stalk, being slightly folded. The eye is quite small, only about one third of the size of the eye of *G. glacialis*.

The arms of *G. glacialis* are about twice as long as those in Sasaki's material and much more slender. The tentacles also appear slightly longer and more slender. The tentacular clubs are quite slender, with very low protective membranes. The club of *G. beringiana*, in contrast, is quite well developed in the holotype. It is clearly expanded, with well-developed protective membranes and dorsal keel. The sucker pedicels are thicker in *G. beringiana*, but the suckers appear to be only slightly larger.

The gladius of *G. glacialis* is broader in the region of the vanes.

In the internal anatomy, only three differences are readily apparent. In *G. beringiana* the stomach extends nearly to the tip of the mantle, terminating in the middle of the fins. The gonad lies at the anterior margin of the fins. The stomach of *G. glacialis* terminates well forward of the fins, and the gonad never extends that far back at the sizes under discussion. The pancreatic tissue of *G. glacialis* extends down the hepatopancreatic duct to the caecum, but there was no sign of this tissue on the duct in *G. beringiana*. The pancreatic lobes are cigar-shaped in *G. beringiana*, while they are more or less spherical in *G. glacialis*.

SUMMARY AND CONCLUSIONS

1. A historical review of the genera *Galiteuthis* Joubin and *Crystalloteuthis* Chun is given.

2. The genus *Crystalloteuthis* Chun, 1906, is synonymized with *Galiteuthis* Joubin, 1898. The principal features separating the two were the presence of complex tubercles at the mantle fusions in the former and the presence of tentacular hooks in the latter. Complex tubercles are shown to occur in *Galiteuthis*, while *C. glacialis*, the type species, develops tentacular hooks at about 60-mm ML. A generic diagnosis is included.

3. The type series of *C. beringiana* Sasaki, 1920 was examined. It conforms to the genus *Galiteuthis*, although the taxonomic status of the species was not determined.

4. *Galiteuthis aspera* Filippova (1972) is synonymized with *G. glacialis* (Chun).

5. The external morphology and internal anatomy of *G. glacialis* are described and illustrated, based on the examination of 824 specimens from 244 stations made by the U.S.N.S. *Eltanin* in antarctic waters. A specific diagnosis is given.

6. *Galiteuthis glacialis* is distinguished from all other cranchiids by the presence of complex tubercles at the nuchal mantle fusion and from other known *Galiteuthis* species by the presence of cartilaginous papillae scattered over the mantle in larger specimens. Arm sucker dentition and shape of the tentacular hook insertion plates may also be diagnostic.

7. Observations of living specimens of *G.*

glacialis in shipboard aquaria showed orientation to be head downward in smaller specimens and tail downward in larger specimens. The change correlates with elongation and thickening of the posterior portion of the gladius, which change the center of gravity.

8. Food preference, from stomach contents, appears to be crustacea, chaetognatha, fish, and miscellaneous organisms, in that order. Cephalopod remains were found in one individual.

9. Growth and development of *G. glacialis* are discussed. Material ranged from 4-mm to 496-mm ML. Standard measurements are compared with mantle length; relationships are linear above 20-mm ML. Tentacular hooks are present, first developing at 55- to 65-mm ML. An olfactory organ is present, contrary to Chun's description.

10. Maximum size and maturity are discussed. A single mature female (496-mm ML) was captured. A very large number of eggs are produced. Eggs were significantly larger in the mature female than in the ovary of the second largest female (397-mm ML) and larger than has been reported for other species, an indication of rapid development prior to spawning. Clarke's hypothesis of gradual maturation and prolonged spawning is rejected for this species. The deteriorated condition of the mature female indicates that death follows spawning.

11. No mature males were seen. The form of the spermatophore is unknown. No external differences were noted between the sexes.

Note added in proof. The manuscript was revised in response to reviewers' comments in September 1973, and subsequent literature has not been noted in the text. Attention is particularly drawn to the recent paper by Dilly and Nixon [1976], which describes the development of another taonine cranchiid squid, *Taonius megalops* Prosch, 1849.

Acknowledgments. This study was first suggested by Gilbert L. Voss and Richard E. Young. I am grateful to Voss for his support and criticism and for the unrestricted use of his personal library. Young's stimulating discussions and thorough knowledge of cephalopod biology greatly influenced the paper. C. F. E. Roper of the Division of Mollusks, U.S. National Museum of Natural History, loaned Sasaki's type specimens and provided references and encouragement. I am indebted to Betty J. Landrum, Supervisor for Records, Smithsonian Oceanographic Sorting Center, for additional data, to Hugh H. Dewitt, Richard McGinnis, John Bradbury, and John Dobrockey for shipboard assistance, to Fay Mucha for histological preparations, to Kathie Jeffries for typing the preliminary drafts, and to Dorothy Blum for typing the final drafts. Illustrations were prepared by my wife, Constance. Financial support was provided by NSF grants GA 709, GA 1493, GB 11127, and GB 24030, G. L. Voss, Principal Investigator. Contribution from the Rosenstiel School of Marine and Atmospheric Science, University of Miami.

REFERENCES

Abel, O.
1916   Paläobiologie der Cephalopoden aus der Gruppe der Dibranchiaten, 281 pp. Gustav Fischer, Jena, East Germany.

Akimushkin, I. I.
1963   Cephalopods of the seas of the U. S. S. R. Institute of Oceanology, Academy of Sciences of the USSR, Moscow. (English translation. Israel Program for Scientific Translations, Jerusalem, 1965.)

Berry, S. S.
1911   Preliminary notices of some new Pacific cephalopods. Proc. U.S. Natn. Mus., *40*(1838): 589-592.

1912   A review of the cephalopods of western North America. Bull. Bur. Fish. Wash., *30*(1910): 269-336, 18 text figs., pls. 32-56.

1917   Cephalopoda. Australasian Antarctic Expedition 1911-1914. Scientific report, Ser. C, *4*(2): 1-39, 5 pls., 30 text figs. Aust. Mus., Sydney.

Bidder, A.
1966   Feeding and digestion in cephalopods. *In* K. Wilbur and C. M. Yonge (Eds.), Physiology of mollusca. *2*: 97-124. Academic, New York.

Chun, C.
1903   Aus den Tiefen des Weltemeers. 2nd ed., 592 pp. Gustav Fischer, Jena, East Germany.

1906   System der Cranchien. Zool. Anz., *31*: 82-86.

1910   Die Cephalopoden. Wiss. Ergebn. Dt. Tiefsee-Exped. 'Valdivia,' *18*(1): 1-410.

Clarke, M. R.
1962a   A large member of the squid family Cranchiidae, *Phasmatopsis cymoctypus* de Rochebrune, 1884. Proc. Malac. Soc. Lond., *35*(1): 27-42, 3 pls.

1962b   Respiratory and swimming movements in the cephalopod *Cranchia scabra*. Nature, *196*(4852): 351-352.

1962c   The identification of cephalopod 'beaks' and the relationship between beak size and total body weight. Bull. Br. Mus. Nat. Hist. Zool., *8*(10): 419-480.

1966   A review of the systematics and ecology of oceanic squids. Adv. Mar. Biol., *4*: 91-300.

Dell, R. K.
1959   Cephalopoda. Rep. B.A.N.Z. Antarct. Res. Exped., Ser. B, *8*(4): 89-106, figs. 1-10.

Denton, E. J., J. P. Gilpin-Brown, and T. I. Shaw
1969   A buoyancy mechanism found in cranchiid squids. Proc. R. Soc., Ser. B, *174*: 271-279.

de Rochebrune, A. T.
1884   Etude monographique de la famille des Loligopsidae. Bull. Soc. Philomath. Paris, Ser. 7, *8*: 1-22, 2 pls.

Dilly, P. N., and M. Nixon
1976   Growth and development of *Taonius megalops* (Mollusca: Cephalopoda), and some phases of its life cycle. J. Zool. Lond., *179*: 19-83.

Filippova, J. A.
1972   New data on the squids (Cephalopoda; Oegopsida) from the Scotia Sea (Antarctic). Malacologia, *11*(2): 391-406.

Grimpe, G.
1922   Systematische Uebersicht der europäischen Cephalopoden. Sber. Naturf. Ges. Lpz., *45-48*: 36-52.

1925   Zur Kenntnis der Cephalopoden-fauna der Nordsee. Wiss. Meeresunters., *16*(3): 1-124.

Hamabe, M.
1961   Experimental studies on breeding habits and development of the squid, *Ommastrephes sloani pacificus* Steenstrup. 2. Spawning behavior. Zool. Mag. Tokyo, *70*(11): 385-394.

1963   Exhaustion process of the genital organs of common squid *Ommastrephes sloani pacificus*. Bull. Japan Sea Reg. Fish. Res. Lab., Engl. Transl., *11*: 1-11

Hoyle, W. E.
1904   A diagnostic key to the genera of recent dibranchiate Cephalopoda. Mem. Proc. Manchr Lit. Phil. Soc., *48*(21): 1-10.

1910   A list of the generic names of dibranchiate Cephalopoda with their type species. Abh. Senckenb. Naturforsch. Ges., *32*: 407-413.

Joubin, L.
1898   Note sur une nouvelle famille de Céphalopodes. Annls. Sci. Nat. Zool., *6*: 279-292, 9 text figs.

Kondakov, N. N.
1941   Cephalopods of the far eastern seas of the U. S. S. R. (in Russian). Issled. Dal'nevost. Morei SSSR, *1*: 216-265.

Mangold, K., and P. Fiorini
1966   Morphologie et biometrie des mandibules de quelques céphalopodes méditerranéens. Vie Milieu, Ser. A, *17*(3A): 1139-1196.

Marchand, W.
1907   Studien ueber Cephalopoden. 1. Der mäanlichen Leitungsapparat der Dibranchiaten. Z. Wiss. Zool., *86*: 311-415.

McSweeny, E. S.
1971   Description of the juvenile form of the antarctic squid *Mesonychoteuthis hamiltoni* Robson. Malacologia, *10*(2): 44-53.

Naef, A.
1921a   Das System der dibranchiaten Cephalopoden und die mediterranen Arten derselben. Mitt. Zool. Stn. Neapel, *22*: 527-542.

1921b   Die Cephalopoden. Fauna Flora Golf. Neapel, monogr. 35, vol. *1*(part 1, no. 1): 1-148, 62 figs., 37 pls.

1922   Die fossilen Tintenfische, 322 pp. Gustav Fischer, Jena, East Germany.

1923   Die Cephalopoden. Systematik. Fauna Flora Golf. Neapel, monogr. 35, vol. *1*(part 1, no. 2): 149-863, 475 figs.

Nesis, K. N.
1972   A review of the squid genera *Taonius* and *Belonella* (Oegopsida, Cranchiidae) (in Russian with English summary). J. Zool., Acad. Sci. USSR, *51*(3): 341-350, 4 figs.

Pfeffer, G.
1912   Die Cephalopoden der Plankton-Expedition. Ergebn. Plankton-Exped., *2*: 1-815, 48 pls.

Robson, G. C.
 1925 On *Mesonychoteuthis*, a new genus of oegopsid Cephalopoda. Ann. Mag. Nat. Hist., Ser. 9, *16*(39): 272-277.

Roper, C. F. E.
 1966 A study of the genus *Enoploteuthis* (Cephalopoda: Oegopsida) in the Atlantic Ocean with a redescription of the type species, *E. leptura* (Leach, 1817). Dana Rep., no. 66, 46 pp.
 1968 Preliminary descriptions of two new species of the bathypelagic squid *Bathyteuthis* (Cephalopoda: Oegopsida). Proc. Biol. Soc. Wash., *81*: 261-272, 7 pls.
 1969 Systematics and zoogeography of the world-wide bathypelagic squid *Bathyteuthis* (Cephalopoda: Oegopsida). Bull. U.S. Natn. Mus., *291*: 210 pp., 12 pls.

Roper, C. F. E., and R. E. Young
 1967 A review of the Valbyteuthidae and an evaluation of its relationship with the Chiroteuthidae (Cephalopoda: Oegopsida). Proc. U.S. Natn. Mus., *123*(3612): 1-9.
 1968 The family Promachoteuthidae (Cephalopoda: Oegopsida). 1. A reevaluation of its systematic position based on new material from the Antarctic and adjacent waters. *In* G. A. Llano and W. L. Schmitt (Eds.), Biology of the Antarctic Seas III, Antarctic Res. Ser., *11*: 203-214, 3 pls. AGU, Washington, D. C.

Roper, C. F. E., R. E. Young, and G. L. Voss
 1969 An illustrated key to the families of the order Teuthoidea (Cephalopoda). Smithson. Contr. Zool., *13*: 1-32.

Sasaki, M.
 1920 Report of cephalopods collected during 1906 by the United States Bureau of Fisheries steamer *Albatross* in the northwestern Pacific. Proc. U.S. Natn. Mus., *57*(2310): 163-203, pls. 23-26.
 1929 A monograph of the dibranchiate cephalopods of the Japanese and adjacent waters. J. Coll. Agric. Hokkaido Imp. Univ., *20*(suppl. 1): 357 pp., 30 pls.

Savage, J. M., and M. C. Caldwell
 1965 Studies in antarctic oceanology. Biological stations occupied by the U.S.N.S. *Eltanin*. Data summary, cruises 1-13, 87 pp. Univ. of S. Calif., Los Angeles.
 1966 Studies in antarctic oceanology. Biological stations occupied by the U.S.N.S. *Eltanin*. Data summary, cruises 14-16 and 18-19, 31 pp., 15 charts. Univ. of S. Calif., Los Angeles.

University of Southern California
 1967 Studies in antarctic oceanology. Biological stations occupied by the U.S.N.S. *Eltanin*. Data summary, cruises 22-24 and 26-27, 31 pp., 15 charts. Univ. of S. Calif., Los Angeles.

Verrill, A. E.
 1881 The cephalopods of the north-eastern coast of America. 2. The smaller cephalopods, including the squids and the octopi, with other allied forms. Trans. Conn. Acad. Arts Sci., *5*: 249-446.

Voss, G. L.
 1963 Cephalopods of the Philippine Islands. Bull. U.S. Natn. Mus., *234*: 180 pp.
 1967a The biology and bathymetric distribution of deep-sea cephalopods. Stud. Trop. Oceanogr., *5*: 511-535.
 1967b Some bathypelagic cephalopods from South African waters. Ann. S. Afr. Mus., *50*(5): 61-88, pls. 1-9.

Williams, L. W.
 1908 Anatomy of the common squid, *Loligo pealei* Lesueur, 92 pp., 3 pl. American Museum of Natural History, New York. (Also E. J. Brill, Leiden, Netherlands.)

Young, R. E.
 1972 The systematics and areal distribution of pelagic cephalopods from the seas off southern California. Smithson. Contr. Zool., *97*: 1-159.

Young, R. E., and C. F. E. Roper
 1967 The Batoteuthidae, a new family of squid (Cephalopoda: Oegopsida) from antarctic waters. *In* G. A. Llano and W. L. Schmitt (Eds.), Biology of the Antarctic Seas III, Antarctic Res. Ser., *11*: 185-202, 6 pls. AGU, Washington, D. C.

The Antarctic Research Series

Each paper submitted to the ARS is thoroughly reviewed by one or more recognized authorities in that discipline. Papers accepted for publication have met the high scientific and publication standards established by the board of associate editors. The members of the current board include Albert P. Crary, Chairman, Charles R. Bentley, Avery A. Drake, Jr., Robert H. Eather, Louis S. Kornicker, Worth D. Nowlin, Jr., and Bruce Parker. Fred G. Alberts, Secretary to the U.S. Advisory Committee on Antarctic Names, gives valuable assistance in verifying place names, locations, and maps.

To get papers into circulation as quickly and economically as possible, a new format has been adopted for the Antarctic Research Series. Papers that have completed the review/revision cycle are assigned by the board of associate editors to a volume according to subject matter and are printed and issued individually as soon as production schedules allow. Several topical volumes may be in process at any time, and the release of an individual paper does not have to wait until all papers proposed for a given volume are ready. The individual papers are issued under soft cover, and pages are numbered consecutively within each volume so that they can be collected and bound together after the last paper is released. At the completion of a volume, subscribers with standing orders will be sent the title page, table of contents, and other front matter for the volume. Purchasers will be responsible for having the volume bound if they choose to do so. Entire volumes will be available on microfiche. Individuals interested in publishing in the series should write to:

Chairman
Antarctic Research Series Board of Associate Editors
American Geophysical Union
1909 K Street, N. W.
Washington, D. C. 20006